TWENTY EVOLUTIONARY BLUNDERS

Dangers and Difficulties of Darwinian Thinking

Randy J. Guliuzza

INSTITUTE FOR
CREATION
RESEARCH

Dallas, Texas
ICR.org

TWENTY EVOLUTIONARY BLUNDERS
Dangers and Difficulties of Darwinian Thinking
BY RANDY J. GULIUZZA, P.E., M.D.

First printing: November 2017

All Scripture quotations are from the New King James Version.

ISBN: 978-1-946246-01-1
Library of Congress Catalog Number: 2017957395

Please visit our website for other books and resources: ICR.org

Printed in the United States of America.

Table of Contents

Introduction

This book takes a historical trip through the scientific literature of evolutionists. It reveals how many of their sensationalized theories have been exposed as chiefly imaginary stories. Each chapter will show how the power of imagination enables scientists to visualize what they are looking for...even when it was never there. The content will highlight key mystical premises of evolutionary theory—specifically, how nature is assumed to have creative intelligence. Evolutionists envision nature as mysteriously exercising creative agency, and they project volitional abilities onto the environment. In addition, each chapter usually teaches something new about the important roles of worldviews, research programs, and so on in the operation of science.

Knowing why these evolutionary blunders are the product of extremely fertile imaginations also explains why they are likely to happen again. A fundamental pillar of evolutionary theory is extrapolation wherein evolutionists observe present-day organisms and must imaginatively visualize backward through vast periods of time to infer what their ancestors were like. The amount of imagination conjured up is proportional to the enormity of time. Darwin himself introduced this inappropriate methodology into scientific research which I have called *look-imagine-see*. Evolutionists *look* at a feature of nature, *imagine* an evolutionary origin, and then *see* what they expect. This book documents that these blunders did not grow out of the tentative, cloudy speculations of hypotheses, but from imaginary stories with vivid details. Another reason to expect a recurrence of more blunders is that Darwin's death-driven evolutionary mechanism is itself not a fully observable process, but includes mystical events which, again, are envisioned only in someone's mind.

A theory is judged by its predictions. So accounting for decades of failed predictions is another good reason to compile the dismal evolutionary track record into a single reference. Before any of the accounts in these chapters were blunders, they were once believed to be a confirmation of an evolutionary prediction. In their heyday, they were unabashedly taught as fact and widely touted as evidence for the strength of evolution. With much fanfare, they did their job of swaying public opinion for evolution—even as scientific research was being misled. But when they were eventually exposed as scientific flops, evolutionists quietly swept them under the rug. They retained discredited materials in textbooks and museum exhibits, and deflected attention toward the self-correcting nature of the scientific method. While exposing them as spectacular blunders may seem to be bashing evolution, it is primarily targeted to demonstrate the weakness of evolutionary theory. If nothing more than for truth's sake, there is a need to bring them to light.

Each topic carefully references the historical background material and the latest literature which should assist as a starting point if further research is desired.

Credit for the idea behind *Twenty Evolutionary Blunders* goes to ICR's CEO Dr. Henry M. Morris III. I am grateful for the editorial expertise of Beth Mull, Truett Billups, Michael Stamp, Christy Hardy, and the Director of Communications Jayme Durant. Dr. Jeffery Tomkins, ICR's geneticist, reviewed my manuscripts, often with the help of ICR's Science Writer Brian Thomas. I'm particularly thankful for my wife June, who also proofread each article and patiently acted as a sounding board for long, and sometimes initially disorganized, monologues which were useful to me for amplifying content on these topics.

1

Evolutionary Predictions
Fail the Reality Test

Summary

Both creationists and evolutionists make predictions based upon their worldview. When it comes to genetics, creationists predicted similarity. However, evolutionists predicted the opposite. They predicted that similar features would have *different* underlying genetics because there's no way millions of years of random mutations, in different ancestral lines, would happen to be the same. Late in the 1970s, *Hox* genes were discovered, and the evolutionists were proven spectacularly wrong. *Hox* genes are similar genetic sequences that program similar features, and they appear in such vastly different creatures such as flies, mice, humans, elephants, and just about every animal in the kingdom. Evolutionist Sean Carroll says, "Disparate animals were built using not just the same kinds of tools, but indeed, the very same genes!" As an amazing confirmation of creation predictions, *Hox* genes show that creatures are the result of common design, not random mutations.

Without a doubt, humans, chimpanzees, and other organisms share similar features. One explanation for the origin of these features is that they reflect similar designs that serve similar purposes. The common design inference is quite intuitive since components of complicated human-designed systems are all directly analogous to other creature's features for similar purposes, such as their structural frameworks, pumps, sensors, and data processors.

For millennia, people willing to hypothesize that God's supernatural design and creativity caused the great diversity of life on Earth have acknowledged the plausibility of the common-design explanation.

Another approach some people use to explain all phenomena is *naturalism,* which closes off any appeal to supernatural intelligence or power and rather presupposes that nature's matter and forces alone are sufficient causes of the origin of the universe and life itself. But naturalism must appeal to mystical mechanisms since people have never observed anything design and create itself by mechanisms that originated purely by nature's matter and forces.

After all, a heart pumping blood through vessels seems to correspond very well in purpose and design to human-made fluid-pumping systems. Should anyone believe that the purposeless, undetectable, mystical intelligence of nature shaped the exquisite details of cardiovascular systems over eons? But a dogmatic commitment to naturalism forces naturalists to construct explanations that are "counterintuitive" and "mystifying to the uninitiated," according to renowned Harvard geneticist Richard Lewontin.[1]

The following chapters compare some of those counterintuitive naturalistic explanations to actual discoveries. This comparison will focus attention on naturalism's largely suppressed but disappointing track record. It has taught many things as factual evidence only to be later revealed as total blunders.

For instance, we know that similarity among creatures extends past body parts to their underlying genetics. Decades in advance of current detailed genetic analysis techniques, creationists and evolutionists alike published expectations based on either intelligent design or evolution, respectively. One test of the accuracy of a scientific model is its ability to make accurate predictions of future research results. Now, these published expectations can be examined in light of new genetic information.

Design-Based Predictions

In 1975, prior to any detailed genetic analysis, ICR founder Dr. Henry Morris asserted there would be common underlying design patterns to explain similar structure. He said:

> The creative process would have designed similar structures for similar functions and different structures for different functions....In the creation model, the same similarities are predicted on the basis of a common purposive designer.[2]

Advocates for design-based explanations knew that organisms, according to their kind, must have similar traits to thrive on the same planet and yet occupy diverse niches. They expected that 1) similar features needed to fulfill similar purposes would be based on similar information, and 2) extreme multistep specified regulation over thousands of details produces unique

11

organisms that may yet have similar overall plans.

Evolution-Based Predictions

Virtually all prominent evolutionists rejected basic common designs, but their rationale differed. Darwin, for theological reasons, doubted "that it has pleased the Creator to construct all the animals and plants in each great class on a uniform plan" and derided the concept of underlying common information as "not a scientific explanation."[3]

In 1963, Harvard's leading evolutionary theorist Ernst Mayr predicted that looking for similar DNA between very diverse organisms would be pointless. He claimed that random genetic changes over millions of years explained the differences in creature's traits and that those many changes would have obliterated genetic similarities.

> Much that has been learned about gene physiology makes it evident that the search for homologous genes [similar codes due to common ancestry] is quite futile except in very close relatives. If there is only one efficient solution for a certain functional demand, very different gene complexes will come up with the same solution, no matter how different the pathway by which it is achieved. The saying "Many roads lead to Rome" is as true in evolution as in daily affairs.[4]

New evolutionary explanations do not explain similarities in organisms whose ancestors supposedly diverged eons ago. *Convergent evolution* is a frequently invoked ancillary explanation, as denoted in Mayr's "Many roads lead to Rome" affirmation. For example, how did naturalists explain diverse creatures possessing eyes made up of similar parts? They claimed that similar environments constrained them to converge on comparable complex features—independently at least 40 times—and probably as many as 65 times.[5]

This explanation, steeped in evolutionary naturalism, counterintuitively claims that millions of years of genetic tinkering somehow propelled organisms to diverge into increasingly different classes while simultaneously cobbling their traits to converge upon "the same solution" to problems.

Creationists, a vocal subgroup of Lewontin's "uninitiated," remained skeptical that similar highly complex structures evolved independently over and over again, but maintained their expectation of finding similar genetic features.

Evolutionary Predictions Spectacularly Wrong

Landmark discoveries between 1978 and 1984 showed the reality of a common genetic basis prescribing how similar structures could be built across diverse groups of organisms.[6] Genes with regulatory and developmental functions responsible for core basic-design patterns in developing embryos are called *Hox* genes (a contraction of longer descriptive words, *homeotic* and *homeobox*). This astounding finding was so opposite to the evolutionists' notions that it clearly constitutes a spectacular blunder on their part. Evolutionary developmental biologist Sean Carroll describes the implications of the stunning details:

> When the sequence of these homeoboxes were examined in detail, the similarities among species were astounding. Over the 60 amino acids of the homeodomain, some mice and frog proteins were identical to the fly sequences at up to 59 out of 60 positions. Such sequence similarity was just

13

stunning. The evolutionary lines that led to flies and mice diverged more than 500 million years ago, before the famous Cambrian Explosion that gave rise to most animal types. No biologist had even the foggiest notion that such similarities could exist between genes of such different animals. The *Hox* genes were so important that their sequences had been preserved throughout this enormous span of animal evolution.[7]

The discovery that the same sets of genes control the formation and pattern of body regions and body parts with similar functions (but very different designs) in insects, vertebrates, and other animals forced a complete rethinking of animal history, the origins of structures, and the nature of diversity. Comparative and evolutionary biologists had long assumed that different groups of animals, separated by vast amounts of evolutionary time, had evolved by entirely different means.[8]

Yet evolutionists remain closed-minded to an explanation of the *Hox* genes' origination by a common designer. They need not concede they were greatly mistaken in their predictions, they were merely "stunned" at the appearance of new unexpected "evidence" for evolution.

But the only "evidence" that *Hox* genes can be "preserved throughout this enormous span of animal evolution" is the belief that life evolved from a common ancestor. All of the stories about convergence get promptly scrapped. Firmly held prior accounts like convergent evolution are run through the magic tunnel of evolutionary belief and *voila*, *Hox* genes somehow turn into "preserved" ancient DNA, which is now used—with equivalent certainty—as evidence of common ancestry.

Design-Based Expectations Confirmed

Now it is factually confirmed that similar genetic regulatory information is common to many classes of organisms and aids in helping achieve similar function—many with remarkably similar designs. Sean Carroll again relates the confounding weight of this finding.

> It was inescapable. Clusters of *Hox* genes shaped the development of animals as different as flies and mice, and now we know that includes just about every animal in the kingdom, including humans and elephants. Not even the most ardent advocate of fruit fly research predicted the universal distribution and importance of *Hox* genes. The implications were stunning. Disparate animals were built using not just the same kinds of tools, but indeed, the very same genes![9]

What about teaching 40 independent occurrences of eye evolution? That manifested as another incredible evolutionary blunder and validation of creationists' design-based expectations. As Carroll candidly continues, "Natural selection has not forged many eyes completely from scratch; there is a common genetic ingredient to making each eye type, as well as to the many types of appendages, hearts, etc."[10]

Is Common Design More Plausible than Common Ancestry?

Could it be that *Hox* genes are the "smoking gun" of common design expected by supporters of intelligent design for decades? Consider this: If engineers were tasked to investigate for common design in any other area, then how would they proceed? They would study various sets of plans and specifications, identify any common features, and verify if there was, in fact, common underlying information. Genetic research identified this common information across diverse groups of organisms. In other areas of research, this fact would be ascribed to common engineering instructions.

Evolutionary theory predicted the complete opposite of common underlying information for similar traits. It was dogmatically taught as evidence for evolution and later found to be profoundly wrong. This catalogs as a spectacular blunder and makes evolutionary teaching misguided at best. These come across scientifically as a mishmash of improvised, after-the-fact stories aimed at forcing observations into an evolutionary paradigm.

Creationists can say with credibility that in creatures as diverse as bacteria, insects, and humans the same genetic information controls the formation and utilization of many key anatomical or molecular structures observed to be performing broadly similar functions.

Applying organism-focused, design-based analysis to biological phenomena brings great clarity to our understanding of life. A compelling case is made that these are clearly the common designs creationists have been looking for over the last 200 years.

References
1. Lewontin, R. 1997. Billions and Billions of Demons. *The New York Review of Books.* 44 (1): 31.
2. Morris, H. 1975. *The Troubled Waters of Evolution.* San Diego, CA: Creation-Life Publishers, 84-85.
3. Darwin, C. 1872. *On the Origin of Species By Means of Natural Selection,* 6th ed. London: John Murray, 383.
4. Mayr, E. 1963. *Animal Species and Evolution.* Cambridge, MA: Harvard University Press, 609.
5. Land, M. F. and R. D. Fernald. 1992. The Evolution of Eyes. *Annual Review of Neuroscience.* 15:1-2,

referencing Salvini-Plawen, L. von and E. Mayr. 1977. On the evolution of photoreceptors and eyes. *Evolutionary Biology.* 10: 207-263.

6. Lewis, E. B. 1978. A gene complex controlling segmentation in *Drosophila. Nature.* 276 (5688): 565-570; Wakimoto, B. T. and T. C. Kaufman. 1981. Analysis of larval segmentation in lethal genotypes associated with the Antennapedia gene complex in *Drosophila melanogaster. Developmental Biology.* 81 (1): 51-64; Scott, M. P. and A. J. Weiner. 1984. Structural relationships among genes that control development: sequence homology between the Antennapedia, Ultrabithorax, and fushi tarazu loci of *Drosophila. Proceedings of the National Academy of Sciences.* 81 (13): 4115-4119; Slack, J. 1984. Developmental biology: A Rosetta stone for pattern formation in animals? *Nature.* 310 (5976): 364-365.

7. Carroll, S. B. 2005. *Endless Forms Most Beautiful.* New York: W. W. Norton & Company, 64.

8. Ibid, 71.

9. Ibid, 65.

10. Ibid, 72.

2

The Eugenics Disaster

Summary

Darwin's survival-of-the-fittest ideas can have deadly social consequences. After evolution gained academic support in the early twentieth century, some scientists and lawmakers enforced their own version of natural selection. They believed that it's our duty to help evolution along. As one prominent evolutionist wrote at that time, "We have to replace the ruthless action of Natural Selection by reasoned conduct in civilized man." The result was eugenics. Its goal was to eliminate "inferior" peoples and breed "superior" peoples. Eugenics was praised in peer-reviewed journals across the world. In America, "inferior" children were forcibly sterilized, "inferior" women were forced to have abortions, the mentally ill were euthanized, and lists of "superior" people were published, encouraging them to mate with each other. It was worse in Germany. Eventually, the situation got so bad that eugenics was condemned and outlawed. Eugenics shows the consequences Darwinism can have on a society, and why it leads to moral decline.

Imagine yourself a young woman diagnosed as "feeble-minded" and trapped in legal proceedings. You take the defense of your personal autonomy to the Supreme Court and finally hear your name in this decision:

Carrie Buck "is the probable potential parent of socially inadequate offspring, likewise afflicted, that she may be sexually sterilized without detriment to her general health and that her welfare and that of society will be promoted by her sterilization," and thereupon make the order. [The "order" is compulsory submission to "the operation of salpingectomy…for the purpose of making her sterile."][1]

In Carrie Buck's failed 1927 Constitutional challenge, the Court upheld a Virginian law that applied Darwinian eugenics. These programs selectively propagated the "fitter," "well born," or "good races" to promote state welfare. In its aftermath, eugenics laws in 31 other states were upheld.

Emboldened by the consensus of scientists, evolutionary research, and then the Supreme Court decision, forced sterilizations of "unfit" citizens increased dramatically throughout the 1930s. Remarkably, sterilizations in some states actually increased *after* World War II.[2]

The tragedy of state-mandated sterilization of those deemed mentally ill or mentally retarded continued into the 1970s.

The final nail in the coffin for state-sponsored sterilization was the 1974 case of Relf v. Weinberger. In Alabama in 1973, officials from the Federal Community Action Program (an anti-poverty program for minorities) took the Relf girls,

Katie, 16, Mary Alice, 14, and Minnie, 12, to a doctor who inserted an IUD in Katie and sterilized Minnie and Mary Alice.[3]

People carry eugenics' scars to this day. Like these 12- and 14-year-old girls, who are now women bearing tubal ligations, Carrie Buck's intelligence was normal all along. She and her husband never had children, and in the United States over 70,000 other victims were compulsorily sterilized, including 8,000 procedures in Lynchburg, Virginia, alone.[4] In other countries, most notoriously Germany, millions suffered the horrors of eugenics programs.

Eugenics was the quest to improve humanity's genetic composition. Eugenicists bred "superior" people and sought to eliminate genetic defects by sterilizing, aborting, or euthanizing "inferiors."[5] Medical applications were developed to mimic nature's "selective" death and loss of reproduction[5] by means of a large-scale implementation of Darwin's belief that through a selective struggle for survival, "the civilized races of man will almost certainly exterminate, and replace, the savage races throughout the world."[6]

Professor Randolph Nesse, a current advocate for Darwinian medicine, candidly admits that the appalling legacy of eugenics-based thinking can be laid squarely on Darwinian evolution. "In the late nineteenth and early twentieth centuries," Nesse says, "most applications were 'medical Darwinism' that focused on the welfare of the species. In connection with eugenics, this led to moral and social disaster."[7] This disaster qualifies as a spectacular evolutionary blunder.

21

Nesse's concession is sparse on details of the link between evolution and eugenics. An explanation from the heyday of eugenics better illustrates why eugenics is wholly indebted to Darwinism. World-renowned British biostatistician Karl Pearson used mathematics to persuasively promote eugenics on three continents from 1900 until his death in 1936. He explains:

> That is, I think, the ever-present fear which the scientific mind recognises: civilised man has largely destroyed crude Natural Selection....In my own mind and in a growing number of other minds...[civilisation will end] unless civilisation can find a method of doing for itself what Natural Selection did for man during his ascent—insuring that he shall breed only from his best. The study of how it is possible forms the subject matter of what we now term the Science of Eugenics. We have to replace the ruthless action of Natural Selection by reasoned conduct in civilised man.[8]

Eugenics: When Humans Determine Survival of the Fittest

It's possible that the eugenics moral disaster is not merely the *misapplication* of Darwinian natural selection but rather the actual *consequence* of that mindset. Death, survival, fitness, and selection are core characteristics of Darwin's concept of natural selection. All are repeatedly stressed in Pearson's influential 1912

United Kingdom Eugenics Society poster from the 1930s when eugenics was popular with scientists. The double meaning of the term "seed" is used in a comparison between spreading healthy plant seed for a bountiful harvest and spreading healthy human "seed" for the purposes of procreating a physically fit, mentally proficient, and racially pure human race.

address to the British Medical Association. Chastising physicians for saving "unfits," he conveyed why all must embrace eugenic applications—and punctuated his points with disturbing photographs of people born with malformed limbs.

Let me…sketch for you the broad outlines of Darwin's theory of evolutionary progress. The individual better fitted to its environment lived longer than its fellows, had more offspring, and these, inheriting its better fitness, raised the type of the race….According to Darwin—and some of us still believe him to be right—the ascent of man, physical and mental, was brought about by this survival of the fitter. Now, if you are going to take Darwinism as your theory of life and apply it to human problems, you must not only *believe* it to be true, but you must set to, and demonstrate that it actually applies….Nevertheless, medical science has to face the fact that the upward progress of man in the past has been largely controlled by stringent Darwinian selection. We shall gain nothing for racial efficiency by neglecting that central fact of human development. Now if there be…a fairly stringent selection of the weaker individuals by the mortality of infancy and childhood, what will happen, if by increased medical skill and by increased state support and private charity, we enable the weaklings to survive and to propagate their kind? Why, undoubtedly we shall have a weaker race…. But we can show from isolated instances that in many ways medical science has led to a survival of the unfit.[9]

At one end of the eugenics spectrum were applications like the marriage registry in the U.S.'s Eugenics Records Office, meant to help people choose "fit" mates from a list of individuals deemed to have desirable inheritable characteristics.[10] Survival-of-the-fittest applications also extended to the spectrum's other end. Charles Epstein, the late president of the American College of Medical Genetics, recounted, "Thus, even if the original notion was of positive eugenics, the actual implementation of eugenic principles very quickly began to run along negative eugenic lines….The object was to ensure the nonsurvival of those considered to be unfit…by prevention of marriage and of racial mixing, institutionalization, sterilization, and sometimes castration." He added, "No longer was breeding of the undesirable to be controlled—rather, the breeders who were thought to carry the undesirable genes were to be eliminated altogether."[11]

Comparable selection-based eugenics beliefs even subtly crept into Christianity. Some claimed that natural selection, though fueled by death, helps the population by getting rid of genetic defects and thus preserves the viability of a population by removing those members with severely harmful or lethal characteristics. They say this exhibits the care of God for His creation in a post-Fall world.

The Euthanasia Society of America started in 1938 as a natural corollary to the movement to prevent "unfit" births. Science historian Ian Dowbiggin documents that members promoted voluntarily and involuntarily euthanizing severely afflicted people. He noted that "mid-twentieth-century American social activists believed that 'birth control' and 'death control' formed 'a rational coalition,' two aspects of the same crusade to liberate human beings from afflictions that had plagued human history for centuries."[12] They viewed "the histories of euthanasia, eugenic sterilization, and birth control in the United States less as separate narratives and more as a single, broad chronicle of events inextricably linked."[13]

How Eugenics Gained Medical Support

Eugenicists employed an effective technique to gain scientific respectability and persuade physicians to act contrary to their medical instincts: peer-reviewed publications. This technique is still useful for obtaining scientific consensus, legislative endorsements, and public acceptance of counterintuitive "scientific" conjectures that carry profound social ramifications—but they may also collapse into enormous blunders.

Scientific journals like the *Annals of Eugenics* and *Eugenics Quarterly* provided peer-reviewed credibility. Major peer-reviewed journals also promoted eugenics, as "from 1910 through 1914 more than 120 articles about eugenics appeared in magazines, a volume of print making it one of the nation's favorite topics....Lobbyists succeeded in part because of favorable views expressed in the medical profession. During the period from 1926 to 1936 about 60 [medical] articles, the vast majority in favor of eugenical sterilization, appeared."[14] Eugenicists thus secured scientific and medical respectability. Later, however, geneticists like Morgan, Pearl, and Haldane demonstrated that persuasive published research was "inadequate" and "old-fashioned rubbish"[15] revealing earlier "veneer review" masquerading as genuine peer review.

For instance, Reilly reported about an influential 1902 study by surgeon Harry C. Sharp of the Indiana Reformatory on the effects of vasectomies performed on 42 inmates. Based on post-sterilization findings of the inmates sleeping better and feeling stronger, his paper advocated "render[ing] every male sterile who passes its portals, whether it be alms house, insane asylum, institute for the feeble minded, reformatory or prison."[16]

The scientific consensus, including prominent faculty from Harvard University and Johns Hopkins Medical School, promoted eugenics as the view of science's progressive thinkers.[17] International Eugenics Congresses were held in 1912, 1921, and 1932, attended by some of the world's leading scientists. Supporters were bestowed high academic honors, while dissenters were usually excluded. Eugenics leaders like America's Harry Laughlin already possessed "expert" status, occupying positions like the Superintendent of the Eugenics Records Office. Their authority was enhanced with actions similar to Laughlin's appointment as Expert Eugenical Agent by a Congressional Committee Chairman in 1921.

Multiple eugenics advocacy organizations were filled with hundreds of prominent academics—though few were geneticists or comprehended the weaknesses in the published literature. Capable researchers critical of eugenics—the minority group—occasionally "shocked" the scientific consensus by publicly questioning tenets of eugenics. The Roman Catholic Church was influential in blocking legislation in some states. Reilly recounts, "Leading eugenicists saw Catholic opposition as their 'greatest obstacle,'" and he adds, "By the mid-1920s eugenicists had recognized the Catholic Church as a major enemy."[18]

In summary, an ardent group advanced their message via media and educational institutions by these means: establish peer review to project credibility, control peer review procedures to muffle critiques, self-coronate "experts" to monopolize authority, and ostracize dissenters to enforce compliance. Through these efforts, eugenicists thoroughly won an international scientific consensus during the first four decades of the twentieth century.

Given its systemic misuse of science, the eugenics legacy was ultimately exposed as such a massive Darwinian blunder that in most literature today "the term [eugenics] is wielded like a club. To label a policy 'eugenics' is to say, in effect, that it is not just bad but beyond the pale."[19] Yet, Darwin's concept of natural selection remains alive and well, so its twisted offspring, eugenics, will no doubt return.

References

1. *Buck v. Bell.* 274 U.S. 200 (1927).
2. Reilly, P. R. 1987. Involuntary Sterilization in the United States: A Surgical Solution. *The Quarterly Review of Biology.* 62 (2): 161.
3. Singleton, M. M. 2014. The 'Science' of Eugenics: America's Moral Detour. *Journal of American Physicians and Surgeons.* 19 (4): 122-125. See also Relf v. Weinberger, 565 F.2d 722 (1977).
4. Wieland, C. 1997. The lies of Lynchburg: How U.S. evolutionists taught the Nazis. *Creation.* 19 (4): 22-23.
5. Weikart, R. 2004. *From Darwin to Hitler: Evolutionary Ethics, Eugenics, and Racism in Germany.* New York: Palgrave Macmillan. Edwin Black documented America's selective breeding and forced sterilization program in Black, E. 2012. *War Against the Weak: Eugenics and America's Campaign to Create a Master Race.* Westport, CT: Dialog Press. See also Guliuzza, R. J. 2009. Darwinian Medicine: A Prescription for Failure. *Acts & Facts.* 38 (2): 32.
6. Darwin, C. 1901. *The Descent of Man.* London: John Murray, 241-242.
7. Nesse, R. M. 2012. Evolution: a basic science for medicine. In *Pragmatic Evolution: Applications of Evolutionary Theory.* A. Poiani, ed. New York: Cambridge University Press, 108.
8. Pearson, K. 1927. *The Right of the Unborn Child, Eugenics Laboratory Lecture Series, No. XIV.* London: Cambridge University Press, 12.
9. Pearson, K. 1912. *Darwinism, Medical Progress and Eugenics; the Cavendish Lecture, 1912, an Address to the Medical Profession.* London: Dulau & Co., Ltd. Published on biodiversitylibrary.org, accessed August 10, 2015. Emphasis in original.
10. Garland, E. A. 1986. The Eugenics Record Office at Cold Spring Harbor, 1910-1940: An Essay in Institutional History. *Osiris.* 2: 227.
11. Epstein, C. J. 2003. Is modern genetics the new eugenics? *Genetics in Medicine.* 5 (6): 469-475.
12. Dowbiggin, I. R. 2002. "A Rational Coalition": Euthanasia, Eugenics, and Birth Control in America, 1940-1970. *Journal of Policy History.* 14 (3): 223.

13. Ibid, 224.
14. Reilly, Involuntary Sterilization in the United States, 154, 161.
15. Ibid, 164.
16. Sharp, H. C. 1902. The Severing of the Vasa Deferentia and its Relation to the Neuropsychiatric Constitution. *New York Medical Journal.* 75: 411-414.
17. Chesler, E. 1992. *Woman of Valor: Margaret Sanger and the Birth Control Movement in America.* New York: Simon & Schuster.
18. Reilly, Involuntary Sterilization in the United States, 164.
19. Paul, D. B. 1998. *The politics of heredity: Essays on eugenics, biomedicine, and the nature-nurture debate.* Albany, NY: State University of New York Press, 97.

3

The Imaginary Piltdown Man

Summary

Evolution demands exceptional imagination. This often leads evolutionists to jump to conclusions and later be proven wrong. In the early twentieth century, *Science* journal reported a fossil discovered near Piltdown, England. Its discoverers claimed the fossil was a human ancestor, called it Piltdown Man, and hailed it as evidence for evolution. However, 40 years later, it turned out to be a complete hoax. Someone had put together a human cranium and an orangutan jaw and duped the entire scientific community. The same thing happened in the early twenty-first century. Another fossil, called Ida, was claimed to be an evolutionary human ancestor. Like Piltdown Man, the hype was enormous...but eventually squashed. Ida was just an extinct lemur. Evolution leads to incredibly fertile imagination that causes scientists to see exactly what they want, regardless of the data. As one evolutionist put it, "We have only to recall the Piltdown adventure to see how easily susceptible researchers can be manipulated into believing that they have actually found just what they had been looking for."

Focused and vividly imagining his next move, the young boy is filled with determination as his mind pictures the football soaring. He runs, positions his legs, and says aloud, "This time I'm gonna kick that ball!" On his back a moment later, a dazed and embarrassed Charlie Brown stares up at Lucy gleefully holding the football and wonders why he fell for her ploy yet again. His oft-repeated blunder over the almost 50 years Charles Schulz produced the *Peanuts* cartoon evidently connected with people who empathized with Brown as either gullible, eternally optimistic, or both.

A mysterious mental interplay exists between imagination, visualization, experience, facts, and beliefs that our mind interprets and reconciles. Likely, these constructs help shape, and are reciprocally shaped by, our worldviews and wills.

Seeing is a sophisticated mental process in which the brain rapidly associates incoming data from the eyes and other sensors with previously learned information stored in the brain. Matching data-information sets are further refined into a sensation we perceive as "sight." Imagination enables someone to form mental images or elaborate sensations that are not necessarily connected to inbound data, stored information, or objective human experience. Careful researchers of evolutionary theory appreciate the constant tension between unavoidable imagination that may produce insightful hypotheses and the reckless gullibility that can lead to embarrassing blunders.

Fertile Imaginations Nourish Evolutionary Theory

The role imagination can play in the mental processing of

data helps explain how someone who believes the naturalistic evolutionary worldview can look at fossil bones and see "transitional" features or look at an odd fish from the ocean depths and see "primitive" features that others don't.

Eminent evolutionist Stephen Jay Gould details why inherent elements of evolutionary theory *must* appeal to our imaginative ability to "see" the unseen things from the past. He describes one such element as *extrapolationism* or scope, in which researchers use "history from data of an imperfect record that cannot, in any case, 'see' past causes directly, but can only draw conclusions from preserved results of these causes." This is accomplished, he says, by explaining "large-scale results by extrapolation from short-term processes…[and] extrapolation to longer times and effects of evolutionary changes actually observed in historic times (usually by analogy to domestication and horticulture)."[1]

Extrapolation in the sense Gould identifies isn't the same as an inferential conclusion but always invokes some imagination to project from the known to the unknown—it fills in the gaps. Intervening time or distance is usually proportional to how much conjecture is summoned; the larger the gap, the more imagination is needed. For instance, what explains the apparent design of interrelated parts in living things? Since people know that design is the cause of multiple parts purposefully working together in man-made things, many people infer that intelligent design is also the cause of such parts in living creatures. However, Darwinists see how organisms can change somewhat in observable time, extrapolate this observation to immense time periods, and imagine radical changes in organisms.

Evolutionary biologist Richard Dawkins explains:

It took a very large leap of the imagination for Darwin and Wallace to see that, contrary to all intuition, there is another way and, once you have understood it, a far more plausible way, for complex "design" to arise out of primeval simplicity. A leap of the imagination so large that, to this day, many people seem still unwilling to make it.[2]

Scientists who question appeals to imagination in lieu of data are merely dismissed by top evolutionary authorities like Jerry Coyne: "It is not valid, however, to assume that, because one man cannot imagine such pathways, they could not have existed."[3] Other such authorities personally disparage critics of illusory evolutionary mechanisms:

Anyone can state at any time that he or she cannot imagine how evolutionary mechanisms might have produced a certain species, organ, structure. Such statements, obviously, are personal—and they say more about the limitations of those who make them than they do about the limitations of Darwinian mechanisms.[4]

Since evolutionists must extrapolate, then people should expect their conclusions to stretch beyond what observable evidence will bear. But when this is pointed out, evolutionists craftily argue that a detractor's inability to imagine a process is not valid evidence against the reality of the imagined process. Nevertheless, because evolutionary theory rests on a pillar of extrapolative imagination—nearly unbridled imagination—there is clearly the susceptibility for interpretive blunders or even outright hoaxes. Therefore, repetitions of these blunders are not simply mistakes.

Seeing What You Always Imagined

On January 17, 1913, America's leading scientific journal, *Science*, described a memorable meeting in England to report "a discovery of the greatest importance…the nearest approach we have yet reached to a 'missing link'…probably few will deny that *Eoanthropus* ["early man"] *Dawsoni* is almost if not quite as much human as simian [higher primate]."[5]

Excitement bubbled over fossil discoveries near Piltdown, England, of an almost totally human cranial cap in close proximity to a partial jawbone nearly identical to that of an ape. *Eoanthropus* fit evolutionary expectations beautifully, in contrast to Eugene Dubois' 1894 report of *Pithecanthropus* ("ape man"), whose humanlike lower limbs and apelike head made scientists "angry and skeptical" because "a being with a human head and an apelike body was expected, not the other way around."[6]

When the *Eoanthropus'* apelike jaw was carefully examined, researchers unmistakably saw that "molars 1 and 2 are typically human," though "their cusps have been worn perfectly flat by mastication [chewing]."[5] Another expert closely inspected impressions on the inside of the humanlike cranium left by arteries housed between the brain and skull. He distinctly saw "the arrangement of meningeal arteries was typically simian, as was a deep notch in the occipital region."[5]

But evidently their minds saw obvious things that weren't really there. *Eoanthropus*, or Piltdown Man, constitutes a major evolutionary blunder. The world's best evolutionists were duped for 40 years before the find was revealed as a forgery in a 1954 *Science* publication. Of course, the article included some excul-

John Cooke's 1915 painting of the Piltdown men: anatomist Arthur Keith in the white coat; behind him to the right, Arthur Smith Woodward, next to Charles Dawson, who made the discovery.

patory commentary that there had always been a few skeptics.[7] This "missing link" consisted of a genuine human cranium and an orangutan's jaw bearing molars manually flattened with a file—all stained with a man-made patina to look ancient. *The New York Times* summed up the situation:

> The skull eventually brought knighthoods to its three leading expositors, Sir Arthur Smith Woodward, Sir Grafton Elliot Smith and Sir Arthur Keith. These learned gentlemen were honored after having spent many years and many pages discoursing on the very human features they discerned in Piltdown man's apelike jaw and the very apelike features they found in his human cranium. The Piltdown skull illustrates the ever-present danger for scientists of seeing what they expect to see.[8]

As evolutionists, these knighted but misguided scientists were rooted in the kind of imaginary extrapolationism that fosters mental constructs that do not exist in a reality outside their minds. And their scientific prodigies are trapped in the same way.

Extrapolation in the 21st Century

On May 19, 2009, researchers held a memorable press conference at the American Museum of Natural History hosted by New York City's mayor to unveil a discovery that purportedly yielded "unprecedented insight into our ancestry." It was headlined as "Fossil Ida: Extraordinary find is 'missing link' in human evolution."[9] Elation boiled over about an alleged 47-million-year-old fossil, *Darwinius masillae*, of a lemur-like animal dubbed "Ida."

Ida's evolutionary significance was evidently in the eye of the beholder. "The more you look at Ida, the more you can see, as it were, the primate in embryo,"[9] stated British naturalist Sir David Attenborough, who narrated the BBC documentary on *Darwinius, Uncovering Our Earliest Ancestor: The Link*. George Washington University anthropologist Brian Richmond summed up his mental picture as: "This specimen looks like a really early fossil monkey that belongs to the group that includes us."[10]

Paleontologist Dr. Jørn Hurum led *Darwinius'* research team and underscored the significance of what they saw: "This will be the one pictured in the textbooks for the next hundred years."[9] His team's credibility was buttressed by the inclusion of University of Michigan's celebrated paleontologist Philip Gingerich, renowned for describing *Pakicetus* ("whale from Pakistan"), a diminutive, long-legged, land-dwelling creature that he "sees" as the ancient ancestor of whales.

However, in little over 100 days, the specter of another overhyped evolutionary blunder loomed as headlines about *Darwinius* read, "Bone Crunching Debunks 'First Monkey' Ida Fossil Hype."[11] This was because *Nature*, a top science journal, published research claiming *Darwinius* was not even close to the same evolutionary grouping as apes.[12]

Hurum defended his view of *Darwinius* by aptly stating that "there's a lot of ways to do cladistics," which intimates that the *Nature* researchers selectively cross-compared fossils and living animals to compile a cherry-picked set of comparative traits—a procedural possibility—to contrive a foreseen cladistics outcome. Thus, Gingerich called the *Nature* team's explanation "implausible."[11] Cherry-picked or not, the critics still ascribed the causality for most of the specimens' similar traits as due to *convergent evolution*, a conclusion that is yet again just an extrapolated mental construct that exists only in the minds of the believers.

Convergence does not flow from objectively discernable causes. It is a declaration based on mental pictures of diverse organisms independently evolving similar traits as they are shaped over time by alleged similar environmental pressures.

Much Evolutionary Science Is a Mental Construct

Certainly, these blunders reinforce some immediate take-home cautions in assessing evolutionary conclusions. Namely, we need to recognize that, in human origins research, fast fame can trump facts. We must realize critical fossil analysis is quite

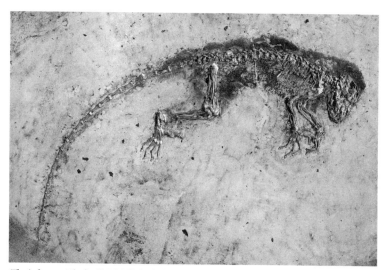

The infamous Ida fossil. Initially hailed as one of the most complete primate fossils ever found and a 47-million-year-old human ancestor, it was revealed only months later to be an extinct lemur.

limited since only a few researchers get to study the specimens firsthand, and much original research, like with *Darwinius*, is carried out in relative secrecy. Remember, history shows that nearly all fossil finds are initially overhyped and under-investigated. Because human origins research can be so subjective, one paleoanthropology researcher voiced a relevant admonition: "We have only to recall the Piltdown adventure to see how easily susceptible researchers can be manipulated into believing that they have actually found just what they had been looking for."[13]

It is important to understand that the scientists' susceptibility to these evolutionary blunders is inextricably tied to their theory-driven need to envision nonexistent things in subjective or fragmentary findings. Fertile imaginations necessarily grow from evolutionary theory's pillar of imaginative extrapolationism, which constantly seeks to craft a storyline for Darwinism. This contentment with mental constructs makes it easier to project human-like volitional abilities onto nature and see it as life's grand designer.[14]

Evolutionists appear to live largely in what could be described as a will-driven reality—i.e., they see what they want to see; they see a past they believe has happened, and that desire drives their vision.

Extrapolating from the known to the unknown exposes the evolutionary theory to robust challenges. Extrapolation is only conceivably plausible if Earth's history has been relatively uniform from a geological, climatic, astronomical bombardment, etc., standpoint. Therefore, every major catastrophe is a challenge to the assumption of uniformity—and the legitimacy to extrapolate. It is also valid to ask: How much of the "evidence" for evolution is only an extrapolated mystical mental construct that is driven more by sheer expectation than science?

References
1. Gould, S. J. 2002. *The Structure of Evolutionary Theory.* Cambridge, MA: Harvard University Press, 59.
2. Dawkins, R. 1986. *The Blind Watchmaker.* New York: W. W. Norton, xii.
3. Coyne, J. A. 1996. God in the Details. *Nature.* 383 (6597): 227-228.
4. Miller, K. 2004. The Flagellum Unspun: The Collapse of "Irreducible Complexity." *Debating Design: from Darwin to DNA.* Ruse, M. and W. A. Dembski, eds. New York: Cambridge University Press, 81-82.
5. Haddon, A. C. 1913. *Eoanthropus Dawsoni. Science.* 37 (942): 91-92.
6. Moore, R. 1962. *Evolution.* New York: Time Incorporated, 132.
7. Straus, W. L., Jr. 1954. The Great Piltdown Hoax. *Science.* 119 (3087): 265-269.
8. Wade, N. New Light on an Old Fraud. *The New York Times,* November 11, 1990.
9. Randerson, J. Fossil Ida: Extraordinary find is 'missing link' in human evolution. *The Guardian.* Posted on theguardian.com May 19, 2009, accessed September 21, 2015.

10. Handwerk, B. "MISSING LINK" FOUND: New Fossil Links Humans, Lemurs? *National Geographic News*. Posted on news.nationalgeographic.com May 19, 2009, accessed September 21, 2015.

11. Keim, B. Bone Crunching Debunks 'First Monkey' Ida Fossil Hype. *Wired Science*. Posted on wired.com October 21, 2009, accessed September 21, 2015.

12. Seiffert, E. R. et al. 2009. Convergent evolution of anthropoid-like adaptations in Eocene adapiform primates. *Nature*. 461 (7267): 1118-1121.

13. Maienschein, J. 1997. The One and the Many: Epistemological Reflections on the Modern Human Origins Debates. *Conceptual Issues in Modern Human Origins Research*. Clark, G. A. and C. M. Willermet, eds. New York: Aldine de Gruyter, 413.

14. Guliuzza, R. 2011. Darwin's Sacred Imposter: Natural Selection's Idolatrous Trap. *Acts & Facts*. 40 (11): 12-15.

4

Survival of the Fittest, Eugenics, and Abortion

Summary

Though eugenics was eventually outlawed, its proponents found new ways of promoting the ideology. Abortion and birth control became their primary cover. In 2014, pre-birth genetic screening was hailed as the "New Eugenics," and dozens of books have been published that resurge eugenics-based ideas, firmly rooted in Darwinism. Peer-reviewed science journals advise doctors to encourage abortion if a patient is expecting a child with "defects" such as Down syndrome. Government programs are designed to "detect and prevent" certain "defects" through pre-birth screening. But pre-birth screening doesn't prevent these defects from entering society—abortion does. As the President of the American Board of Medical Genetics says, "Does prenatal diagnosis involve deprivation of life? The answer, in real terms, is certainly yes." And so the Darwinian ideology of eugenics continues under the name of abortion.

Western society's eugenics disaster of the early 20th century sought to weed out the "unfit"—people seen as genetically dragging the human race down. It flowed from a survival-of-the-fittest mentality.[1] The U.S. Supreme Court punctuated this blunder with the *Buck v. Bell* decision (1927) that effectively legalized eugenics practices. Though eugenics became widely stigmatized by the 1970s, a captivating fitness-survival-death mindset endured. These death-fueled practices haven't missed a step following the Supreme Court's *Roe v. Wade* (1973) decision that legalized abortion, the *new* eugenics.

The Eugenics-Abortion Link

Early eugenicists won a scientific consensus by using a few strategies. They established peer review to secure credibility, abused peer review to monopolize control, crowned "experts" to project authority, and marginalized dissenters to enforce compliance.[1] Though the public found forced sterilization distasteful, recent research by social scientists Deborah Barrett and Charles Kurzman reveal how eugenicists perpetuated their practices right under society's nose. They document how eugenics-driven peer review continued by merely renaming the existing periodicals. The *Annals of Eugenics* transitioned to the *Annals of Human Genetics*, *The Eugenics Review* conveniently became *The Journal of Biosocial Science,* and *The Eugenical News/Eugenical Quarterly* morphed into *Social Biology.*[2]

Noting that eugenics-based ambitions were purposefully channeled into abortion-rights activities, they added,

> In keeping with the subterranean strategy, some eugenicists continued their work under the cover of non-eugenic

disciplines and organizations, such as the birth-control and population-control movements. For example, the first administrator of the Population Council, a former president of the American Eugenics Society, recalled in 1974 that the post-war birth-control and abortion-rights movements were great eugenic causes, but "[if] they had been advanced for eugenic reasons it would have retarded or stopped their acceptance."[105] Eugenic ideals such as racism, paternalism, scientific authority, and genetic manipulation did not disappear from the world, and were arguably institutionalized in certain wings of the reproductive sciences.[3]

Like cancer, eugenics spread into another death-driven method of population control: abortion. The old eugenics regrew into a new eugenics. With its atrocious history, how could this happen?

The Root Cause of Eugenics

While eugenics qualifies as a spectacular evolutionary blunder by all accounts, Professor Randolf Nesse accurately does *not* point the finger at evolution in general but specifically at Darwinian natural selection. Nesse says, "Most applications were 'medical Darwinism' that focused on the welfare of the species. In connection with eugenics, this led to moral and social disaster."[4]

Darwinism is predicated on death eliminating "unfit" members from populations of creatures as they struggle to survive. Darwinian *selection* as the root concept nurturing eugenics was unmistakably affirmed by a leading proponent during its heyday in 1927.

43

In my own mind and in a growing number of other minds… [civilization will end] unless civilisation can find a method of doing for itself what Natural Selection did for man during his ascent—insuring that he shall breed only from his best. The study of how it is possible forms the subject matter of what we now term the Science of Eugenics. We have to replace the ruthless action of Natural Selection by reasoned conduct in civilised man.[5]

That ruthless understanding of Darwinism continues unabated today even in diverse realms. Notably, a recent article critical of the Amazon Corporation quoted a former human resources director claiming that the company implemented "purposeful Darwinism." This referred to some employees as winners and others as losers who leave or are fired in annual staff cullings.[6]

Unfortunately, those opposing eugenics, abortion, and euthanasia today often point at evolution as fostering these behaviors, but that blame may not be fully on target. Death-driven behaviors are tenaciously rooted in the fitness-survival-death mindsets that encompass Darwinian thinking. But those who embrace these ideas may not even realize this connection. By default, evolutionists must champion natural selection, but various non-evolutionists profess to be big fans also. Indeed, even some Christians claim that natural selection, though fueled by death, helps the population by getting rid of genetic defects and thus preserves the viability of a population by removing those members with severely harmful or lethal characteristics. They believe this process somehow exhibits God's care for His creation in a post-Fall world.

Given the broad support for natural selection and that survival-of-the-fittest has not been targeted as a cause for today's death-culture mentality, it isn't surprising that eugenics is resurging within the context of "evolution."

Eugenics Is Resurging Today

A 2014 headline in a popular newspaper read "Let's (Cautiously) Celebrate the 'New Eugenics,'"[7] written by a senior research fellow at the University of California-Davis. He describes a new form of eugenics applied through pre-birth genetic screening by medical experts. Genetics tests before or after conception may determine if an unborn child might have a serious disorder.

Preventing genetic diseases is one end of a continuum that leads to dreams of genetically enhancing humans at the other end. Predictably, evolutionist Richard Dawkins dared ask the eugenics-reviving question: "Why [is it] acceptable to train fast runners and high jumpers but not to breed them?" He adds, "But hasn't the time come when we should stop being frightened even to put the question?"[8]

Today's eugenicists, as explained in "The Eugenic Impulse,"[9] still think that crafting humanity using evolutionary methods is noble. The agenda appears in books like *Redesigning Humans*, *Radical Evolution*, *Enhancing Evolution*, *More Than Human*, and *The Price of Perfection*. A 2012 essay in *The Chronicle of Higher Education* details the evolutionary root that is responsible for society's interest in eugenics. The author, a Johns Hopkins medical historian, highlights why eugenicists "cannot resist the allure of taking control of our own evolution, of engineering our future."

"Eugenics is the self-direction of human evolution," proclaimed the poster for the 1921 International Eugenics Congress. It is this sense of eugenics that Maynard Olson, Matt Ridley, and others are invoking. For example, in *Enhancing Evolution*, John Harris proposes "both the wisdom and the necessity of intervening in what has been called the natural lottery of life, to improve things by taking control of evolution and our future development to the point, and indeed beyond the point, where we humans will have changed, perhaps into a new and certainly into a better species altogether."[9]

Genetic information is medically valuable. Yet, genetic "engineering" of society—via elimination of those "unfavored" by nature's lottery—threatens us with another colossal evolutionary blunder implemented by reckless experts. Just like 120 years ago, they still come armed only with the medical knowledge of the day, channeled through agendas crafted by human wisdom that is further disadvantaged by fitness-survival-death beliefs.

Answering two questions is vital: 1) How do today's citizens get informed on genetics-based eugenics, and 2) what outcome is expected when they are equipped with that information? Today's answers foreshadow a repeat of government or expert coercion that leads to deadly outcomes.

Before the formalization of government eugenics programs, eugenics was promoted in 1912 by coercing prospective parents via a twisted version of the relationship between doctors and their patients. Britain's leading eugenicist implored doctors to swap unbiased presentations of information for subtle pressure on patients during counseling. He writes,

> But great as is the influence of medical opinion on public action, it is more than equalled [*sic*] by the weight which the individual medical man can exert in his private relationship either as a consultant or as a family doctor. He is the confidential friend of many men and women, and as such in a quiet and unobtrusive way he can do much to encourage the fit to parentage and discourage the unfit.[10]

That tactic inspires today's eugenicists. A 1998 worldwide survey of over 2,900 genetics professionals found a strong association between eugenics-based thinking and the goals of genetics in medicine.[11] Furthermore, this research revealed that "directiveness" in counseling, based on pessimistically biased information of persons with genetic disabilities, influences parental decisions after prenatal diagnosis. Information delivered by genetics professionals underlies "patient education and consent"—the first step in healthcare provision. Only voluntary consent is truly valid. Consent that is given under persuasion is manipulation. Voluntary decisions mature from deliberations of accurate information and not misinformation that stigmatizes certain disabilities.

Depending on circumstances and how information is presented, when counselors tell patients the current "standard of care," or "weigh the impact on the family," or even consider "the needs of financially strained healthcare systems," patients could be facing coercion.

Certainly, the government has enormous financial interests in prenatal screening. A comprehensive report on the cost effectiveness of California's prenatal screening program in 1999 estimated lifetime medical costs of $450,000 for a person with Down Syndrome.[12] These researchers disclose how the government intends to avoid paying that money:

> For evaluation purposes and to assess the benefits of the Program, NTD [neural tube defect], AWD [abdominal wall defect], and Down Syndrome were selected as the major birth defects that the Program was designed to detect and prevent.[12]

Prevent? Screening doesn't "prevent" people with these conditions from entering society—abortion does. Further, the report labels events for the government as "missed opportunities" when citizens are informed that their child will have Down syndrome and still choose life over abortion.

Death-driven behaviors follow in a society so steeped in survival-of-the-fittest thinking that scholars recently set a perverse tone for explanations of how *beautiful* creatures emerged over time, all starting with, "In a cut-throat world where only the fittest survive…."[13] When fitness-survival-death notions are even used to teach children why dog hair lengths vary in different niches, then death can be invoked as an avenue toward good for everything.

Today's eugenics-abortion link is stronger than ever. One President of the American Board of Medical Genetics plainly affirmed,

> I come now to the final question regarding prenatal diagnosis and eugenics—does prenatal diagnosis involve deprivation of life? The answer, in real terms, is certainly yes. What-

ever the theory might be with regard to prenatal diagnosis as merely providing information, prenatal diagnosis and abortion are inextricably linked.[14]

After 63 million abortions in the United States since 1973, including the selling of aborted babies' body parts, isn't it time to adopt origins explanations that condemn death-driven methods and promote a culture of life?

"For You formed my inward parts; You covered me in my mother's womb. I will praise You, for I am fearfully and wonderfully made; Marvelous are Your works" (Psalm 139:13-14).

References
1. Guliuzza, R. J. 2015. The Eugenics Disaster. *Acts & Facts.* 44 (11): 10-12.
2. Barrett, D., and C. Kurzman. 2004. Globalizing social movement theory: The case of eugenics. *Theory and Society.* 33: 487-527.
3. Ibid, 514. Reference 105 within the quote is from Meehan, M. 1998. How Eugenics Birthed Population Control. *The Human Life Review.* 24: 78.
4. Nesse, R. M. 2012. Evolution: a basic science for medicine. *Pragmatic Evolution: Applications of Evolutionary Theory,* Aldo Poiani., ed. New York: Cambridge University Press, 108.
5. Pearson, K. 1927. *The Right of the Unborn Child, Eugenics Laboratory Lecture Series, No. XIV.* London: Cambridge University Press, 12.
6. Kantor, J., and D. Streitfeld. Inside Amazon: Wrestling Big Ideas in a Bruising Workplace. *The New York Times.* Posted on nytimes.com August 15, 2015, accessed October 20, 2015.
7. Entine, J. Let's (Cautiously) Celebrate the "New Eugenics." *Huffington Post.* Posted on huffingtonpost.com October 30, 2014, accessed October 28, 2015.
8. Dawkins, R. From the Afterword. *Herald Scotland.* Posted on heraldscotland.com November 19, 2006, accessed October 20, 2015.
9. Comfort, N. The Eugenic Impulse. *The Chronicle of Higher Education.* Posted on chronicle.com November 12, 2015, accessed October 20, 2015.
10. Pearson, K. 1912. *Darwinism, Medical Progress and Eugenics; the Cavendish Lecture, 1912, an Address to the Medical Profession.* London: Dulau & Co., Ltd, 28.
11. Wertz, D. C. 1998. Eugenics Is Alive and Well: A Survey of Genetic Professionals around the World. *Science in Context.* 11 (3-4): 493-510.
12. Cunningham, G. and D. Tompkinson. 1999. Cost and effectiveness of the California triple marker prenatal screening program. *Genetics in Medicine.* 1 (5): 199-206.
13. Maxmen, A. 2015. Animal behavior: Come mate with me. *Nature.* 526 (7572): S8-S10.
14. Epstein, C. J. 2003. Is modern genetics the new eugenics? *Genetics in Medicine.* 5 (6): 469-475.

5

Our Useful Appendix—Evidence of Design, Not Evolution

Summary

Darwin started the whole "vestigial organ" thing. He speculated that since creatures are the result of random mutations, then they should be full of useless organs that are the remnants of a long evolutionary process. That evolutionary speculation continues today. In particular, the human appendix has been promoted as a "vestigial organ," an organ without function, and hailed as evidence of humanity's evolutionary past. Evolutionist Jerry Coyne called it a "nefarious organ." But then, of course, that all changed. In 2015, secular scientists discovered that the appendix plays an important role in maintaining the health of the digestive system. As predicted, evolutionists found a way to incorporate that function into their theory, claiming "it makes evolutionary sense." Allegedly "vestigial" organs continue to show function, making evolutionists scramble to rework their theory, and confirming that creatures were indeed designed by a Creator.

Once there was a teenage girl with a sweet personality, selfless spirit, and diverse skills. But she was so envied by her cruel stepmother and two rude stepsisters that they constantly forced her to do the nastiest jobs in almost total obscurity. The Cinderella story is so universally appealing that it has been translated into over 60 languages and made into multiple films. In these types of stories, the perpetrators' bigotry reflects their constrained mindset. The worthy becomes worthless in their view.

Belief systems matter.

This is also true in origins research. Some belief systems liberate thinking. Others, like an evolutionary worldview, are so confining that evolutionary biologists may either observe non-existent or overlook actual biological functions based on preconceived notions of what they expect to see.[1] One example of this bias is the categorization of the human appendix as a worthless organ by thought-constrained evolutionists. This assumption hindered research on a truly useful part of our digestive system and highlights a colossal evolutionary blunder.

The "Useless" Appendix Is "Evidence" for Evolution

Since Darwin's time, the world's sharpest evolutionary biologists have championed the human appendix as unquestionable evidence *for* evolution and *against* intelligent design. But scientific research demonstrates the folly of both assertions by showing the appendix to be a fully functional organ.

Darwin cultivated a scientifically regrettable practice that still persists today. He imagined an evolution-caused loss of function for certain biological structures and declared them to be essentially useless—without ever seeking to understand their purpose. In 1874 Darwin said,

> With respect to the alimentary canal, I have met with an account of only a single rudiment, namely the vermiform appendage of the caecum....It appears as if, in consequence of changed diet or habits, the caecum had become much shortened in various animals, the vermiform appendage being left as a rudiment of the shortened part....[Regarding humans] not only is it useless, but it is sometimes the cause of death.[2]

In 2007, over 130 years later, Francisco Ayala, the president of the American Association for the Advancement of Science announced, "A familiar rudimentary organ in humans is the vermiform appendix....The human vermiform appendix is a functionless vestige of a fully developed organ present in other mammals," adding the punchline "Vestiges are instances of imperfections—like the imperfections seen in anatomical structures—they argue against creation by design but are fully understandable as a result of evolution by natural selection."[3]

Ernst Mayr, another giant in evolutionary circles and former Director of Harvard's Museum of Comparative Zoology, provided a definition of a vestigial feature. He said it was "a deconstructed, nonfunctional characteristic that had been fully functional in a species' ancestor, like the eyes in cave animals and the human appendix."[4]

Like Darwin, rather than search for a science-based discovery of function, Mayr fills the knowledge gap with a story that nearly deifies nature by projecting "protective" and "selective" powers onto the environment. He confidently asserts, "Many organisms have structures that are not fully functional or not functional at all. The human caecal appendix is an example.... When these structures lose their function owing to a shift in lifestyle, they are no longer protected by natural selection and are gradually deconstructed." Mindful to slip in the vital implications for beliefs about origins, Mayr pronounces, "These three phenomena—embryonic similarities, recapitulation, and vestigial structures—raise insurmountable difficulties for a creationist explanation, but are fully compatible with an evolutionary explanation based on common descent, variation, and selection."[5]

Dr. Jerry Coyne, emeritus professor of biology at the University of Chicago, repeatedly offers the appendix as evidence against design. In 2005 he explained, "The human body is also a palimpsest of our ancestry. Our appendix is the vestigial remnant of an intestinal pouch used to ferment the hard-to-digest plant diets of our ancestors....An appendix is simply a bad thing to have. It is certainly not the product of intelligent design: how many humans died of appendicitis before surgery was invented?"[6]

Then in his 2009 definitive work *Why Evolution Is True*, Coyne affirms, "We humans have many vestigial features proving that we evolved. The most famous is the appendix." To punctuate the point, he inserts a bit of sarcasm: "Discussing the appendix in his famous textbook *The Vertebrate Body*, the paleontologist Alfred Romer remarked dryly, 'Its major importance would appear to be financial support of the surgical profession.'" Finally, summing up, "In other words, our appendix is simply the remnant of an organ that was critically important to our leaf-eating ancestors, but of no real value to us."[7]

These are definitive conclusions that the appendix is undeniable evidence *for* evolution and *against* creation. The result? By the mid-20th century, thousands of "prophylactic" surgeries had been performed based on assumptions that "the sooner [vestigial appendages] are removed the better for the individual."[8] Unfortunately, these recommended surgeries flowed from evolutionary beliefs rather than scientific findings.

Evolution's Declarations Are Spectacularly Wrong

"Immune cells make appendix 'silent hero' of digestive health" was the November 30, 2015, headline for a report on recent research in *ScienceDaily*.[9] The story made plain that "new research shows a network of immune cells helps the appendix to play a pivotal role in maintaining the health of the digestive system, supporting the theory that the appendix isn't a vestigial—or redundant—organ." The study found that cells in our gut and appendix interface directly with intestinal microbes to regulate colonies of bacteria. The appendix facilitates recovery from threats to gut health by repopulating the gut with "good" bacteria.

One primary researcher quoted by *ScienceDaily* focused specifically on popular unfounded beliefs.

Professor Gabrielle Belz, a laboratory head in the [Walter and Eliza Hall Institute] Molecular Immunology division, said the study's findings show that the appendix deserves more credit than it has historically been given. "Popular belief tells us the appendix is a liability," she said. "Its removal is one of the most common surgical procedures in Australia, with more than 70,000 operations each year. However, we may wish to rethink whether the appendix is so irrelevant for our health."[9]

Nature Immunology published the original research that found that "interplay between intestinal ILC3 cells and adaptive lymphocytes [types of white blood cells] results in robust complementary failsafe mechanisms that ensure gut homeostasis [stability]."[10]

Belz's findings reinforce earlier research. A 2007 Duke University Medical School press release challenged Darwinism's naïve view of the appendix: "Long denigrated as vestigial or useless, the appendix now appears to have a reason to be—as a 'safe house' for the beneficial bacteria living in the human gut."[11] Informed researchers would neither be surprised nor make such a blunder since medical textbooks have identified functioning lymphoid tissue in the appendix for decades.

Detecting Darwinian Spin

In the face of scientific data confirming the appendix's usefulness, what could an evolutionist do? One option is to quickly admit the blunder and tell colleagues not to rescue the appendix argument—lest vain defenses compound blunder upon blunder. But the customary salvage approach, as Paul Ehrlich classically observed, is to stretch their super-elastic theory to engulf *any* observation—even conflicting ones.[12]

To put a positive spin on Duke's discovery of the appendix's usefulness, evolutionists exploited their theory's elastic nature. In light of the decades-old claim that a useless appendix was evidence for evolution, Brandeis University biochemistry professor Douglas Theobald's response to a useful appendix was, "It makes evolutionary sense."[13]

In 2009 when Coyne wrote *Why Evolution Is True*, he was aware that the appendix "may be of some small use. The appendix contains patches of tissue that may function as part of the immune system. It has also been suggested that it provides a refuge for useful gut bacteria." But in the face of evidence inconsistent with the appendix as vestigial, he still spins a case for evolution by insisting that "the appendix is still vestigial, for it no longer performs the function for which it evolved."[14] To understand Darwinian selectionism, people must master the art of spotting circular reasoning. Coyne's thinking is essentially assumptive—he knows evolution happened because the appendix is vestigial. And how does he know it's vestigial? Because it no longer performs the function for which it evolved.

Later, Coyne flatly states, "Our appendix is a nefarious organ" that no designer would own up to and that undoubtedly is one of many "evolutionary leftovers." Thus, Coyne asks what everyone should be thinking: "So why do we still have one?" His speculations reflect the quintessential Darwinian explanation, which projects mystical powers onto nature and is otherwise beyond the realm of human verification. And since these speculative claims can't be verified empirically, they are readily accepted as valid explanations. He says, "We don't yet know the answer. It may in fact have been on its way out, but surgery has almost eliminated natural selection against people with appendixes. Another possibility is that selection simply can't shrink the appendix any more without it becoming even *more* harmful."[15]

However, selection may not be shrinking anything. *Science* reported that the appendix is more widespread in mammals than believed. Evolutionists now explain—enter elastic spin again—this surprising finding as the independent evolution of appendices between 30 to 40 times in different kinds of animals.[16]

The Appendix: A Well-Designed Organ

Belief systems matter. Creationists infer that since organisms and sophisticated human-made things have similar characteristics that they were both designed and crafted for a purpose. Evolutionists tend to deify a "natural selector," favoring some random genetic mistakes that can either shrink organs or cobble them together from scratch. When evolutionists cannot immediately determine the function of an organ, they imagine how it could have lost its function and declare it basically useless. Biases inherent to belief systems can force adherents into faulty conclusions. The appendix blunder does not just indicate shoddy scientific research, it reveals the faulty belief system which drives evolutionary assumptions.

Therefore, when presented with an appendix whose function is an enigma, what should an unbiased researcher do? Study it with diligence and objectivity and draw conclusions from real evidence.

The appendix is strategically situated like a sentry at the entrance to the microbe-filled colon in the gut of every creature that possesses one. The appendix tissue that interfaces with microbes both reseeds and regulates microbe types as it performs vital digestive functions in the colon. The dynamic self-regulation of gut microbes helps these organisms to eat different diets and relocate into new niches. It's just one example of many types of innate self-adjusting mechanisms,[17] which are always indicators of intentional design.

The human appendix, "long denigrated as vestigial or useless," is in reality a "silent hero" providing "robust complementary failsafe mechanisms" for good intestinal health. Kind of sounds like a Cinderella organ...and one having very good design.

References

1. Guliuzza, R. 2015. Major Evolutionary Blunders: The Imaginary Piltdown Man. *Acts & Facts.* 44 (12): 12-14.
2. Darwin, C. 1874. *The Descent of Man, and Selection in Relation to Sex,* 2nd ed. London: John Murray, 20-21.
3. Ayala, F. J. 2007. *Darwin's Gift to Science and Religion.* Washington, DC: Joseph Henry Press, 91.
4. Mayr, E. 2001. *What Evolution Is.* New York: Basic Books, 291.
5. Ibid, 30-31.
6. Coyne, J. The Faith That Dare Not Speak Its Name: The case against intelligent design. *New Republic.* Posted on uchicago.edu August 22 and 29, 2005, accessed December 1, 2015.
7. Coyne, J. 2009. *Why Evolution Is True.* New York: Viking, 60-61.
8. Rabkin, W. 1955. The Pros and Cons of Tonsillectomy. *South African Medical Journal.* 45 (1): 30.
9. Walter and Eliza Hall Institute. Immune cells make appendix 'silent hero' of digestive health. *ScienceDaily.* Posted on sciencedaily.com November 30, 2015, accessed December 1, 2015.
10. Rankin, L. C. et al. Complementarity and redundancy of IL-22-producing innate lymphoid cells. *Nature Immunology.* Published online before print November 30, 2015.
11. Duke University Medical Center. Appendix Isn't Useless at All: It's a Safe House for Bacteria. *ScienceDaily.* Posted on sciencedaily.com October 8, 2007, accessed December 17, 2015.
12. Ehrlich, P. and L. Birch. 1967. Evolutionary History and Population Biology. *Nature.* 214 (5086): 349-352.
13. Appendix May Produce Good Bacteria, Researchers Think. *Associated Press.* Posted on foxnews. com October 5, 2007, accessed on December 4, 2015.
14. Coyne, *Why Evolution Is True,* 61-62.
15. Ibid, 81, 62.
16. Barras, C. Appendix Evolved More Than 30 Times. *Science.* Posted on sciencemag.org February 12, 2013, accessed December 6, 2015.
17. Tomkins, J. 2012. Mechanisms of Adaptation in Biology: Molecular Cell Biology. *Acts & Facts.* 41 (4): 6.

6

Are Whales and Evolution Joined at the Hip?

Summary

Darwin imagined a lot of things. One of them was that bears evolved into whales. The belief that a fully land-dwelling mammal returned to the water and transformed into whales persists in evolutionary literature. Evolutionists point to the "vestigial" hind legs in a whale as evidence, but, like the appendix, new research found function for this "vestigial organ." It plays a vital role in reproduction in watery environments, giving whales greater mobility and control. In response, Darwinists give it an evolutionary spin. "Co-option" is the explanation. Whale legs are vestigial, but were co-opted for another use. This shows the pliability of evolutionary theory, and how it continues to offer failed predictions.

National Geographic has a *Little Kids First Big Book of...* series on different topics. In its *Little Kids First Big Book of Animals*, pictures show giraffes, camels, bears, and whales.[1] Young readers can see they all look different. Animals that live on land, like bears, have legs. But no one has seen a whale with legs. However, upon closer look, bears and whales do have some of the same traits. They both give birth to live young and nurse their offspring. Some whales also have hair in particular places on their body. These similar traits mean that both bears and whales are mammals. Some land mammals swim in the water a lot. What would happen if one type started to live more in the water than on land? Would its front legs slowly change to flippers like a whale has? Would its back legs gradually disappear? Is it possible that over a long time one kind of land animal could even become a whale?

The Evolutionary Origin of Whales

Some evolutionists imagined that whales could evolve from an animal like a bear. Charles Darwin considered how black bears can swim for a long time. Once he wrote about such bears

> ...swimming for hours with widely open mouth, thus catching, like a whale, insects in the water. Even in so extreme a case as this, if the supply of insects were constant, and if better adapted competitors did not already exist in the country, I can see no difficulty in a race of bears being rendered, by natural selection, more and more aquatic in their structure and habits, with larger and larger mouths, till a creature was produced as monstrous as a whale.[2]

This scenario flows from a very fertile imagination. But, as documented in an earlier chapter, imaginary extrapolation is a key element of evolutionary theory.[3]

Darwin's thought about a bear-like animal evolving into

whales is now seen more as an illustration than a reality. For many years, evolutionists believed that whales evolved from an extinct carnivorous mammal group called *mesonychids*. Their interpretation of fossils supported their conclusion. Ernst Mayr said in 2001, "A beautiful series of intermediate stages also exists between the mesonychid ungulates and their descendants, the whales."[4]

But now most evolutionists reject the mesonychids as ancestors for whales. Instead, important new fossils discovered in Pakistan are interpreted as filling that role. DNA sequences were also compared between whales and living animals that have features similar to those of the new fossils. Evolutionists now have "a firm understanding" that whales evolved from an animal more related to giraffes and camels.[5] Unfortunately, "substantial discrepancies remain" between interpretations of fossil data and results from DNA studies, according to Johns Hopkins University professor Kenneth Rose.[6] Rose and others explain that similarities between whales and mesonychids happened independently in both groups due to "convergent evolution." Convergence is not an observation flowing from objectively discernable causes. It is actually a declaration based on mental pictures of diverse organisms evolving similar traits as they are shaped over time by alleged similar environmental pressures.

There are still substantial discrepancies between DNA and fossil evidence for whale evolution. But evolutionists remain convinced that "the transition from a primitively quadrupedal terrestrial ancestor to a convergently 'fish-like' modern mammal species" actually happened in a process that "involved changes in numerous character systems." Definitely not understating the point, they add that "almost all anatomical systems of living cetaceans are highly modified for an aquatic lifestyle, with dramatic changes seen in...limbs."[7]

Whale Hip Bones as Evidence for Whale Evolution

Speaking of limbs, evolutionists believe they see greatly reduced pelvis or hip bones in some whales. They teach this observation as hard evidence for whale evolution. Just like the human appendix,[8] these "hip" bones are interpreted as a vestigial structure. Jerry Coyne from the University of Chicago sums up the evolutionary position nicely:

> Whales are treasure troves of vestigial organs. Many living species have a vestigial pelvis and leg bones, testifying...to their descent from four-legged ancestors. If you look at a complete whale skeleton in a museum, you'll often see the tiny hindlimb and pelvic bones hanging from the rest of the skeleton, suspended by wires. That's because in living whales they're not connected to the rest of the bones, but are simply imbedded in tissue. They once were part of the skeleton, but became disconnected and tiny when they were no longer needed.[9]

For decades, evolutionists did not search for any other uses for these bones. Why? Because they expected to find a *vestigial* pelvis.

Declarations About Whale Hip Bones Were Wrong

Fortunately, two researchers were not fully content with the customary explanation. In light of their research, the standard

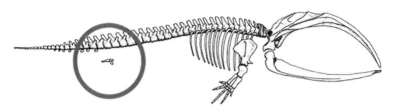

Scientists may struggle to admit a blunder. They seem prone to try to save it. These "hip" bones are not attached to the backbones of living whales, dolphins, or any of the fossils.... The assertion that these bones are hip bones or a pelvis is a mystical claim.

evolutionary story about whale hip bones, as relayed by Coyne, appears to be another major evolutionary blunder.

Matthew Dean of the University of Southern California and Jim Dines of the Natural History Museum of Los Angeles County examined "hip" bones in whale and dolphin skeletons. Their painstaking research of more than 10,000 unsorted bones turned "a long-accepted evolutionary assumption on its head." According to the report, "common wisdom has long held that those bones are simply vestigial, slowly withering away like tailbones on humans." But their results "[fly] directly in the face of that assumption, finding that not only do those pelvic bones serve a purpose—but their size and possibly shape are influenced by the forces of sexual selection."[10] This new analysis of whale hips was published in the scientific journal *Evolution*.[11]

Dines and Dean are evolutionists. They still believe that whales evolved from a four-legged land mammal. Thus, they believe that they really are studying vestigial hip bones. But, as reported, "'everyone's always assumed that if you gave whales and dolphins a few more million years of evolution, the pelvic bones would disappear. But it appears that's not the case,' said Matthew Dean."[10]

These bones serve an important purpose. In fact, "the muscles that control a cetacean's penis—which has a high degree of mobility—attach directly to its pelvic bones. As such, it made sense to Dean and Dines that the pelvic bones could affect the level of control over the penis that an individual cetacean has, perhaps offering an evolutionary advantage."[10]

Dean and Dines are not likely to say that their research highlighted another evolutionary blunder over beliefs about vestigial organs. But Dean did admit that "our research really changes the way we think about the evolution of whale pelvic bones in particular, but more generally about structures we call 'vestigial.' As a parallel, we are now learning that our appendix is actually quite important in several immune processes, not a functionally useless structure."[10]

Salvaging the Darwinian Whale Hip Story

Scientists may struggle to admit a blunder. They seem prone to try to save it. These "hip" bones are not attached to the backbone of living whales, dolphins, or any of the fossils. Claims beyond the realm of human detection are mystical—like the assertion that these are hip bones or a pelvis. Thus, Coyne's defense that whale "hip" bones are truly vestigial remnants invokes mysticism.

Salvage efforts may force even more mystical appeals. Coyne acknowledges that whales use the bones during reproduction. But as to the conclusion that the bones are not vestigial, he adds, "This argument is wrong: no evolutionist denies that the remnants of ancestral traits can retain some functionality or be co-opted for other uses."[12] For evolutionists, reproductive functions are simply co-opted from a locomotive function. Co-option is not an observation. Rather it is a declaration. When does a researcher observe co-option happening? Because, if you think about it, every part of a human has more than one function. Co-option is summoned to fit ill-fitting findings into evolutionary theory.

Evolutionists also try to work some fossil evidence into their land mammal-to-water mammal evolutionary scenario. Included are fossils discovered in Southwest Asia of four-legged creatures with a true pelvis. They have essentially no resemblance to whales. However, the evolutionary community embraced research that asserted they were a primitive type of whale. Whales and dolphins are categorized as cetaceans. These fossil creatures were given names like *Ambulocetus* and *Pakicetus*, which place them in the same category. But how does one know that these are truly fossils of the evolutionary ancestor of whales? Obtaining convincing proof is difficult. But changing the definition of what constitutes a whale is easier.

An article titled "What Is a Whale?" in *Science* dealt with the issue of deciding whether *Ambulocetus* was in the whale's lineage. It reasonably noted, "Another problem arises considering that discoveries of ostensible whales occur fairly regularly...with new combinations of characters making it difficult to decide whether they are whales following a strictly character-based definition." In other words, shouldn't a creature have most of the distinctive characteristics of whales in order to be called a whale? The problem facing evolutionists was how to include *Ambulocetus* into the whale category in spite of its clear lack of whale-like features. Thus, they determined that "a more reasonable solution is to use a phylogenetic definition [for whales], that is, one based on common ancestry....*Ambulocetus* is a whale by virtue of its inclusion in that lineage."[13]

But the point of the research was to see if *Ambulocetus* was enough like whales to rationally be included in whales' lineage. Changing to a new phylogenetic definition is shrewd. It enables evolutionists to simply declare *Ambulocetus* to be a whale by virtue of their prior declaration that it is an ancestor to whales.

Abdominal Bones Well-Designed for a Key Function

ICR's Brian Thomas provided an excellent synopsis on the whale bone research.[14] He described the problems with seeing these bones as evolutionary adaptations. He offered a better explanation of bones designed for a specific purpose. The bones in the lower abdomen in some whales do not connect to other bones but are embedded in several muscles. Bone provides a firm anchor for other structures that are manipulated by these muscles. It seems that these bones may be vital for extraordinarily large bodies to mate in a fluid environment. Similarly, many animals and also humans have a bone called the *hyoid* in their neck region. It also is affixed only by muscles above and below it. The hyoid provides a firm anchor for these muscles to help manipulate the tongue, larynx, and pharynx. Both the hyoid and whale abdominal bones are a good design solution for the movement of accessory structures.

In light of recent research, why shouldn't these bones be renamed in the scientific literature? Could simply using the given names "whale hip bones" or "whale pelvis" mislead people? Evolutionary literature makes subtle changes to the normal usage of words like whale, gene, selection, and evolution. Readers should be alert for this ploy. In this case, changing the definition of a whale allowed fossils with a true pelvis to fit into evolutionists' story of whale evolution. There are other consequences. National Geographic may need to change animal names in their *Little Kids First Big Book of Animals*. With continual word manipulation by evolutionists, little kids themselves may soon struggle to do something they normally excel at: identifying giraffes, camels, bears, and whales.

References

1. Hughes, C. D. 2010. *National Geographic Little Kids First Big Book of Animals*. Washington, DC: National Geographic Society.
2. Darwin, C. 1859. *On the Origin of Species by Means of Natural Selection*. London: John Murray, 184.
3. Guliuzza, R. 2015. Major Evolutionary Blunders: The Imaginary Piltdown Man. *Acts & Facts*. 44 (12): 12-14.
4. Mayr, E. 2001. *What Evolution Is*. New York: Basic Books, 63.
5. Spaulding, M., M. A. O'Leary, and J. Gatesy. 2009. Relationships of Cetacea (Artiodactyla) Among Mammals: Increased Taxon Sampling Alters Interpretations of Key Fossils and Character Evolution. *PLOS ONE*. 4 (9): e7062.
6. Rose, K. D. 2001. The Ancestry of Whales. *Science*. 293 (5538): 2216-2217. See also Spaulding, et al., 11.
7. Spaulding, et al., 1.
8. Guliuzza, R. 2016. Major Evolutionary Blunders: Our Useful Appendix—Evidence of Design, Not Evolution. *Acts & Facts*. 45 (2): 12-14.
9. Coyne, J. A. 2009. *Why Evolution Is True*. New York: Viking, 60.
10. Perkins, R. Whale Sex: It's All in the Hips. University of Southern California news release. Posted on pressroom.usc.edu September 8, 2014, accessed January 12, 2016.
11. Dines, J. P. et al. 2014. Sexual selection targets cetacean pelvic bones. *Evolution*. 68 (11): 3296-3306.
12. Coyne, J. The Faith That Dare Not Speak Its Name: The case against intelligent design. *The New Republic*. August 22, 2005.
13. Berta, A. 1994. What Is a Whale? *Science*. 263 (5144): 180-181.
14. Thomas, B. Vital Function Found for Whale 'Leg' Bones. *Creation Science Update*. Posted on ICR.org October 6, 2014, accessed January 13, 2016.

7

The "Poor Design" of Our Recurrent Laryngeal Nerve

Summary

As usual, starting with Darwin, evolutionists point to alleged examples of poor design as evidence for their theory. One of the main examples is the nerve that controls the human vocal cords. It runs between them and the brain. It is called the *recurrent laryngeal nerve*, or RLN. However, it takes a circuitous route. Instead of going from the brain straight to the vocal cords, it runs down around the heart. According to evolutionist Jerry Coyne, the left RLN is "one of nature's worst designs." But, unsurprising, the RLN turns out to be well-designed. Mainstream studies have shown that it provides mechanical support for a vessel connected to the heart while a baby develops in the womb, making sure the vessel functions properly after birth. Evolutionists continue to use current ignorance of biological functions as evidence for their theory, but whenever we make a new discovery, creation speaks clearly of wise design.

"There you go again" is Ronald Reagan's unforgettable line from his 1980 United States presidential election debate with incumbent President Jimmy Carter. This pithy phrase is not insulting but is certainly less than flattering. It is meant to characterize an opponent's claim as a worn-out, ill-conceived falsehood.

Well, "there you go again" fits David Barash's recent *Wall Street Journal* opinion piece. Titled "Imperfect Reproductions," it parroted the tired evolutionary assertion that human bodies are Exhibit A for all things poorly designed.[1] Barash, an evolutionary psychologist, was thrilled to review Jeremy Taylor's book *Body by Darwin*,[2] which itemizes several alleged examples of how the human body reflects an evolutionary history. Many evolutionists believe that sticking a "poor design" tag onto a creature's traits constitutes scientific evidence *against* creation and *for* evolution. But that line of thinking is beset with problems.

Opinions that an Intelligent Designer would not be a poor designer, though reasonable, are theological in nature, not scientific. Nonetheless, many evolutionists believe that pursuing evidence for poor design is a scientific search. However, classifying a structure as "poorly designed" amounts to little more than another area of discussion involving evolutionary extrapolation (i.e., imagination).[3] There is no objective test for poor design. So, how do evolutionists look at a feature and see poor design?

Seeing poor design invokes as many there-you-go-again flights of imagination as seeing creatures with "primitive" or "transitional" features, seeing nature select, or seeing convergent evolution. These are all mystical mental constructs that are

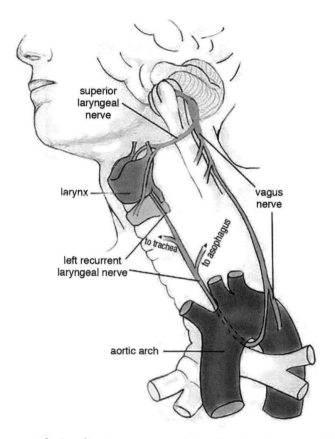

only mental visualizations, not realities flowing from tangible observations. However, secular scientists' naturalistic worldview compels their persistent quest to find nature's poor designs.

Evolutionists Believe Nature Blindly "Cobbles Together" Organisms

The expectation of poor design is inseparable from the belief that mindless nature is life's creator. How could nature shape organisms? Boston University's vocal and dogmatic evolutionary biologist David Levin recently outlined how he thinks nature slowly cobbles together organisms. First, random mutations in a creature's DNA are caused by nature's forces. Later, nature dispenses death to the unfit, whereby nature selects only the fittest survivors, and in this way "natural selection is the sculpting of the genome by the environment."[4]

Sculpting? A reader may be misled to think of the artistic attention to detail exhibited by Michelangelo. Levin's sculpting, in contrast, comprises millions of imagined genetic tweaks honed through struggle and death over eons. The only supporting evidence for the sculpting process envisioned by Levin is that he sees many designs that his own mind characterizes as "poor." But neither the sculpting process nor the classification of poor design is based on objective observations.

Evolutionists, such as Levin, believe this ubiquitous process is inherently unplanned, a hodgepodge affair. Two evolutionary biologists hold that "regulatory [genetic] elements that are cobbled together, incorporating binding sites [in the genome] for multiple collaborating transcription factors to take advantage of an existing landscape of developmental regulators, appear to be common."[5] Other evolutionary researchers claim that "the discovery that the hemoglobins of jawed and jawless vertebrates were invented independently provides powerful testimony to the ability of natural selection to cobble together similar design solutions using different starting materials."[6] It appears that even though nature cannot exercise any detected agency, the minds of Darwinists readily project onto nature incredible creativity and resourcefulness.

Lists of "poorly designed" human structures include eyes, throats, and birth canals, along with molecular features like the blood-clotting cascade and DNA itself. Evolutionists also assert that one long nerve in our neck, the recurrent laryngeal nerve (RLN), not only reflects poor design but is evidence that we long ago descended from fish. As additional scientific information is gained, these claims are being exposed as one major evolutionary blunder after another. Examination of the RLN reveals its "poor design" claim to be another classic blunder.

The "Maladaptive" Recurrent Laryngeal Nerve

Vocal cords in the larynx are innervated by the right and left laryngeal nerves. These nerves branch off of their respective vagus cranial nerves. On the left side, the vagus nerve travels from the skull, down the neck, toward the heart, and then past it. The recurrent laryngeal nerve branches off from the vagus just below the aorta. Then, looping under the aorta the RLN travels upward (or recurs) to serve several organs as it travels up to the larynx. Evolutionists see poor design in the fact that the left nerve does not branch off closer to the larynx. (It should be noted that even though the left RLN is longer than the right nerve, signals to each nerve are adjusted so that the vocal cords are stimulated simultaneously so normal speech is produced.)

Suppose an advocate for Intelligent Design debated Dr. Jerry Coyne, emeritus professor of evolution at the University of Chicago. "There you go again" would be a fitting response to his list of poor designs. In *Why Evolution Is True*, Coyne affirms that "one of nature's worst designs is shown by the recurrent laryngeal nerve in mammals. The curious thing is that it is much longer [about two feet longer] than it needs to be." He later adds, "This circuitous path of the recurrent laryngeal nerve is not only poor design, but might even be maladaptive."[7]

He claims that the only reasonable explanation for the route of the nerve is that it originally started out innervating gills in fish. Later, amphibians evolved from fish and reptiles, and mammals evolved from them. Then, he says, "during our evolution" as our heart moved into our chest (unlike fish) "to keep up with the backward evolution of the aorta, the laryngeal nerve had to become long and recurrent" up to our larynx (which fish also don't have).[7]

Paleontologist Donald Prothero echoes, in another "there you go again" conclusion, the same assertion: "Not only is this design wasteful, but…the bizarre pathway of this nerve makes perfect sense in evolutionary terms. In fish and early mammal embryos, the precursor of the recurrent laryngeal nerve [is] attached to the sixth gill arch, deep in the neck and body region."[8]

These are definitive declarations, considered undeniable evidence of poor design and evolution.

The RLN: Evolutionary Declarations Are Stunningly Wrong

Scientific literature published over a decade prior to either Prothero's or Coyne's book detailed a very good reason why the RLN loops under the aortic arch. The RLN plays several key roles during a baby's pre-birth development, one of which is absolutely vital and quite intriguing.

To set the stage, we know that while a baby develops in his

mother's womb, he is living in a watery world in which his lungs are not functioning for oxygen exchange. Therefore, most blood bypasses the lungs through some temporary shunts. One shunt is a small artery with a very muscular wall that connects the pulmonary trunk to the aorta. Its Latin name is *ductus arteriosus*. When the baby takes his first breath upon birth, the artery detects specific signals, and the muscular wall constricts in order to close the vessel. Blood is now forced into the lungs. Why does the *ductus arteriosus* have such a muscular wall compared to other blood vessels that have far more elastic fibers?

Investigations at Johns Hopkins Medical School found that during development, "the left vagus nerve and its recurrent laryngeal branch form a sling supporting the distal (or *ductus arteriosus* component) of the left sixth aortic arch." Remarkably, these researchers found in their study that

The media [composition of the blood vessel wall] of the ductus arteriosus beneath the supporting nerves is thinner and has less elastic fiber formation than the elastic lamellar media of the adjacent aortic arches. The study shows that the vagus and recurrent laryngeal nerves are in a position to provide mechanical support to the ductus arteriosus during its development and that the morphology [or composition] of the media of the supported ductus arteriosus differs from that of the adjacent unsupported aortic arches. It is suggested that this local mechanical support may be the reason that the normal ductus arteriosus differentiates as a muscular artery and is therefore able to obliterate its lumen in postnatal life. Without such support the ductal media could develop the abundant elastic fibers characteristic of the normal unsupported aorta and pulmonary trunk and become an abnormal, persistently patent [or open] ductus arteriosus [not a good situation].[9]

Developmental research shows how the RLN could be seen as a wise mechanism, designed to provide the right supporting conditions during a baby's development for the *ductus arteriosus* to form correctly. There are multiple purposes for this nerve beyond activating the left vocal cord. Its length, location, and function all point to ingenious—not poor—design. The assertion that its position in our body is due to a remote fish ancestry is yet another colossal evolutionary blunder.

"Poor Design" Is an Assertion Made from Ignorance

When they present a "poor design" argument, critics usually demonstrate a profound lack of knowledge of the structures they fault. Their criticisms are not backed up by people who actually conduct research on those parts. Though these critics may not know what they are talking about in regard to function, there are other problems with their argument.

From a design perspective, the blunder over the RLN clearly shows that evolutionists may be unaware of the need to balance several competing interests. This principle of design is known as *optimization*. Because a design doesn't maximize the performance of the one particular trait capturing evolutionists' interest, they don't think it relevant to search out whether the entity as a whole was designed. They may be ignorant of good reasons for design tradeoffs between various traits, as well as other traits yet to be discovered. Balancing design tradeoffs is difficult work. It is a powerful indicator of intelligence behind a design.

But even if a claim of poor quality were true, that alone would not undermine design. Items designed by humans range in quality from careless to extremely fine. Quality in itself is not the sign of intellectual activity. Genuine design does not demand anything be of the best quality. Questioning *how* something was designed has nothing to do with the question of *whether* it was designed.

Poor Design: Real or Imaginary?

"There you go again" would be a good reply to Dr. Abby Hafer's new book, *The Not-So-Intelligent Designer: Why Evolution Explains the Human Body and Intelligent Design Does Not*.[10] It would also be fitting when Jerry Coyne says, "In clear and lively prose, [Kenneth] Miller shows that complex biochemical pathways are cobbled together from primitive precursor proteins that once had other functions but were co-opted for new uses."[11]

When reading evolutionary literature, be sensitive to the fact that you will hear many words that misrepresent reality and substitute fantasies for observation. Such writings habitually personify nature as being able to "cobble together," "invent," and exercise agency through "natural selection [as] the sculpting of the genome by the environment."[12] It is legitimate to ask how much of the Darwinian process is just a phantasm that exists only in one's mind. No wonder that extrapolating evolutionary theory to real life leads to one blunder after another.

Worldviews matter. Creationists infer that since organisms and sophisticated human-made things have analogous characteristics, they were both designed and crafted for a purpose.

Environmental elements alone do not achieve even shoddy design, since they have not been shown to produce *any* design. There is absolutely no need from the outset to ever concede that anything on creatures is poorly designed. In reality, creatures in their prime normally exhibit breathtaking fit and finish. For most people, the complexity and near-perfect function in living things are "clearly seen"[13] (Romans 1:20) and absolutely amazing.[14]

References
1. Barash, D. Imperfect Reproductions. *The Wall Street Journal.* Posted on wsj.com January 29, 2016, accessed February 4, 2016.
2. Taylor, J. 2015. *Body by Darwin: How Evolution Shapes Our Health and Transforms Medicine.* Chicago, IL: The University of Chicago Press.
3. Guliuzza, R. J. 2015. Major Evolutionary Blunders: The Imaginary Piltdown Man. *Acts & Facts.* 44 (12): 12-14.
4. Spetner, L. M. Information and mutation—Responding to David Levin. *Evolution News and Views.* Posted on evolutionnews.org February 2, 2016, accessed February 5, 2016.
5. Hersh, B. M. and S. B. Carroll. 2005. Direct regulation of knot gene expression by Ultrabithorax and the evolution of cis-regulatory elements in Drosophila. *Development.* 132 (7): 1567-1577.
6. Simons, T. Biologists find that red-blooded vertebrates evolved twice, independently. University of Nebraska-Lincoln news release. Posted on newsroom.unl.edu July 26, 2010, accessed February 9, 2016.
7. Coyne, J. 2009. *Why Evolution Is True.* New York: Viking, 82-84.
8. Prothero, D. R. 2007. *Evolution: What the Fossils Say and Why It Matters.* New York: Columbia University Press, 37-38.
9. Leonard, M. E., G. M. Hutchins and G. W. Moore. 1983. Role of the vagus nerve and its recurrent laryngeal branch in the development of the human ductus arteriosus. *American Journal of Anatomy.* 167 (3): 313-327.
10. Hafer, A. 2015. *The Not-So-Intelligent Designer: Why Evolution Explains the Human Body and Intelligent Design Does Not.* Eugene, OR: Cascade Books.
11. Coyne, J. A. Seeing and Believing: The never-ending attempt to reconcile science and religion, and why it is doomed to fail. *The New Republic.* Posted on newrepublic.com February 3, 2009, accessed December 29, 2015.
12. Spetner, Information and mutation—Responding to David Levin.
13. Guliuzza, R. J. 2010. Fit & Function: Design in Nature. *Acts & Facts.* 39 (2): 10-11.
14. For an informative review of the important role of the RLN, see Bergman, J. 2010. Recurrent Laryngeal Nerve Is Not Evidence of Poor Design. *Acts & Facts.* 39 (8): 12-14.

8

Berra's Blunder

Summary

Evolutionists love slippery terms. The most common one is their namesake *evolution* that Adrian Bejan defines as "flow organization (design) that changes over time." The generality of this definition makes it uncontroversial—but almost useless. A common argument for evolution uses this kind of slippery definition, equates creatures to man-made machines, and then says that common ancestry "explains itself." This is called *Berra's Blunder*. It supposes that one can simply line up a series of similar-looking objects to demonstrate evolution. Adrian Bejan does this with airplanes. He looks at the way airplane design changed during the twentieth century, likens that to the fossil record, and then invokes a slippery definition of evolution to argue for common ancestry. However, this argument suffers from a number of difficulties. The main one is so obvious that it seems silly to have to point it out: Man-made machines were *designed*. If one were to equate them to creatures, then it seems

81

that an Intelligent Designer would be the natural conclusion—not random evolution.

Did you know airplanes evolve? A 2014 research article titled "The Evolution of Airplanes," written by Duke University's distinguished Professor of Mechanical Engineering Adrian Bejan, makes that very claim.[1] He begins with all the visible differences between a biplane and a jumbo jet. Airplanes have gotten bigger and faster over the decades. We could say airplane design evolves in the sense that it changes over time.

A second look reveals some common features like engines and wings. What is the best way to explain both the similarities and differences at the same time? Are we seeing a core common design enhanced with many ingenious variations? Or did all modern airplanes descend from a common, primitive airplane ancestor, evidenced by similar ancestral traits but with new features adapted to new conditions? These questions sound a lot like those asked by evolutionists and creationists about living creatures. Bejan wrote his article to supply those answers.

Falsely Linking Airplane Design to Biological Evolution

First, we must know what Bejan means by "evolve." He zig-zags in his definition, initially saying, "Evolution means a flow organization (design) that changes over time." The generality of this definition makes it uncontroversial—but almost useless. However, it eases acceptance of the far more specific, hotly disputed theory of evolution. For the rest of the paper, he uses biological evolution in the sense of a universal common ancestor that gave rise to life's diversity by a long, natural process of modified descent. Bejan argues that the evolution of the "human-and-machine species" clearly depicts Darwinism.

His premise raises a couple of questions. Why must Bejan conjure up a "human-and-machine species" (whatever that is)? Can we reasonably assume that any "evolution" we observe in this mystical species accurately reflects natural processes?

Bejan makes a telling disclosure about evolutionary theory as he explains why we can't use real organisms as examples of evolution.

In biology, evolution is largely a mental construct built on imagination, because the time scale of animal evolution is immense relative to the time available to us for observations. We cannot witness animal evolution, and this places the biology argument for evolution at a disadvantage. It would be useful to have access to the evolution of one species in real time....The species to watch is the human-and-machine species.[1]

The centerpiece of his case is the article's Figure 1, which depicts "the evolution of the major airplane models during the 100-yr [sic] history of aviation." After readers carefully study this figure, Bejan contends that descent with modification will be so self-evident that these new insights will "open everybody's eyes to the natural phenomenon called 'evolution.'"[1]

Though evolutionists think this argument is solid, Bejan actually makes a common evolutionary blunder. He supposes that just by looking at a succession of variants from anatomical traits, DNA sequences, or fossils that diverge from a norm that descent with modification is the self-evident explanation. But merely lining up successions of similar-looking objects fails as scientifically adequate proof of evolution.

One problem is that studying pictures of airplanes does not by itself provide evidence about any evolutionary mechanisms. Unless a plausible biological mechanism capable of answering our key questions is provided, these pictures are only linked by imagination. Neither Figure 1 nor the remainder of Bejan's research paper describes the evolutionary mechanism.

Another problem is that lining up one set of anatomical traits compared to different sets of traits could give two completely different successions. Or lining up several creatures' anatomical traits compared to their DNA sequences and supposed fossil ancestors could give at least *three* different evolutionary stories.

The most obvious problem is the availability of another equally valid, if not superior, explanation. When people look at different kinds of airplanes, they know from experience that the real explanation for similarities and differences is engineering processes that come from the minds of real engineers. The most rational conclusion is that a core common design was enhanced with many ingenious variations.

Berra's Blunder

Evolutionists like Bejan often point to the slow, successive modification of man-made things over time as examples of how they interpret fossils or DNA sequences. However, this is known as *Berra's Blunder*.

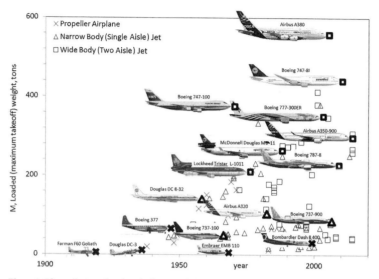

Figure 1: The evolution of major airplane models during the 100-year history of aviation.

Former UC Berkeley Law School Professor Phillip E. Johnson coined the term "Berra's Blunder" in his 1997 book *Defeating Darwinism by Opening Minds*. In one section titled "Learn the difference between intelligent and unintelligent causes," he explains why this should be a basic proficiency for all advocates of intelligent design. He uses several illustrations to show how "this is a distinction that many otherwise capable scientists do not understand."[2]

One of Johnson's examples is evolutionary biologist Tim Berra. In his 1990 book *Evolution and the Myth of Creationism: A Basic Guide to the Facts in the Evolution Debate*, Berra says, "Everything evolves, in the sense of 'descent with modification,' whether it be government policy, religion, sports cars, or organisms." He applies evolution to Chevrolet's Corvette Stingray automobile to illustrate his point. He says, "If you compare a 1953 and a 1954 Corvette, side by side, then a 1954 and a 1955 model, and so on, the descent with modification is overwhelmingly obvious. This is what paleontologists do with fossils, *and the evidence is so solid and comprehensive that it cannot be denied by reasonable people.*"[3]

Berra summarizes everything by claiming that the causal mechanism of change between living creatures and man-made Corvettes is the same:

> The point is that the Corvette evolved through a selection process acting on variations that resulted in a series of transitional forms and an endpoint rather distinct from the starting point. A similar process shapes the evolution of organisms.[3]

Johnson's analysis spots several logical blunders. His concise reply demonstrates that either he is not a reasonable person (as Berra claims) or that he is truly a lucid thinker:

> Of course, every one of those Corvettes was designed by engineers. The Corvette sequence—like the sequence of Beethoven's symphonies to the opinions of the United States Supreme Court—does not illustrate naturalistic evolution at all. It illustrates how intelligent designers will typically achieve their purposes by adding variations to a basic design plan. Above all, such sequences have no tendency whatever to support the claim that there is no need for a Creator, since blind natural forces can do the creating. On the contrary, they show that what biologists present as proof of "evolution" or "common ancestry" is just as likely to be evidence of common design.[4]

86

Those who commit Berra's Blunder usually combine two elements. First, they miss how reasonable people might explain similarities and differences in a variety of ways simply because they have different perspectives. They overlook other possibilities, fixate on common descent, and insist that it is the only explanation.

Second, they also neglect to rightly distinguish between intelligent and unintelligent causes. They see an engineer exercise agency and then assume nature can exercise a similar type of agency. Advocates of design should be trained to spot Berra's Blunder in evolutionary literature, such as the succession of airplanes within Bejan's "The Evolution of Airplanes" paper. Once the blunder is spotted, just calling it Berra's Blunder summarizes the discussion.[5]

Lessons Learned from Berra's Blunder

Darwin set the stage for his followers to make Berra's Blunder. It flows from the circular mental picture depicted in his writings. For him it was self-evident that common descent explains similar features. Darwin concludes, "The similar framework of bones in the hand of a man, wing of a bat, fin of the porpoise, and leg of the horse…and innumerable other such facts, at once *explain themselves* on the theory of descent with slow and slight successive modification."[6] Circular arguments are naturally self-certifying. Thus, common ancestry explains similar features, and similar features explain common ancestry. This is an axiom in evolutionary biology, an obvious truth to be assumed and used as a general explanation. Apparently, it does not need experimental validation.

Accordingly, Bejan truly does expose that "the biology argument for evolution [is] at a disadvantage" since "evolution is largely a mental construct built on imagination."[1] This is no trivial observation. Bejan, like Berra, shows how their successions have no real observable intermediates. They are only conceptual. Fertile imagination, not evidence, fills the gaps. Conceptual intermediates join other major evolutionary presumptions like co-evolution, co-option, nature exercising agency, and convergent evolution. None of these flow from observations of discernable causes but are actually *declarations* built on mental pictures. One must ask: How much of the evolutionary scenario exists only in an evolutionist's mind rather than reality?

Why does this problem of unbridled imagination persist? Evolutionary authority Stephen Jay Gould said that a "pillar" of evolutionary thought is *extrapolationism*, or scope. Evolutionists explain "large-scale results by *extrapolation* from short-term processes…[and] extrapolation to longer times and effects of evolutionary changes actually observed in historic times (usually by analogy to domestication and horticulture)."[7] Extrapolation, in the sense Gould identifies, is not the same as an inference. It always invokes imagination to project from the known to the unknown—it's clearly speculation. Intervening time or distance is usually proportional to how much conjecture is summoned. The larger the gap, the more extrapolation and imagination are needed.

However, similar features linked with imagination are not enough to establish whether two or more distinct entities are closely, remotely, or totally unrelated in ancestry. Just comparing similar features—or even DNA—to determine related ancestry is virtually always an inference with a probability of being right ranging from high to essentially zero. True relationships are fact-based connections, like a line of connected birth certificates.

The good news is that it doesn't take any imagination to see the flying performance of an airplane or the phenomenal capability of birds. Bejan wonderfully documents how flying animals "converge on the same design—the same scaling rules—as the evolution of human fliers [airplanes]," and "yet, airplanes obey allometric rules that unite them with birds and other animals."[8] The same principles of design that exploit natural properties enable flight in both airplanes and birds. That fact is clearly seen.

Human engineering can be pretty amazing. The far-superior aerial acrobatics capability of birds testifies to the engineering genius of the Lord Jesus Christ.[9] Let's learn to recognize both elegant design in nature and the massive blunders evolutionists use to explain it away.

References

1. Bejan, A., J. D. Charles, and S. Lorente. 2014. The evolution of airplanes. *Journal of Applied Physics*. 116 (4): 044901.
2. Johnson, P. E. 1997. *Defeating Darwinism by Opening Minds*. Downers Grove, IL: InterVarsity Press, 62-63.
3. Berra, T. 1990. *Evolution and the Myth of Creationism: A Basic Guide to the Facts in the Evolution Debate*. Stanford, CA: Stanford University Press, 117-119. Emphasis in original.
4. Johnson, *Defeating Darwinism by Opening Minds*, 63.
5. Halley, K. Going overboard with Darwinian analogies. *Creation Ministries International*. Posted on creation.com November 7, 2015, accessed March 1, 2016; Luskin, C. Karl Giberson and Francis Collins Commit Berra's Blunder While Arguing for Macroevolution. *Evolution News and Views*. Posted on evolutionnews.org May 19, 2011, accessed March 1, 2016; Wells, J. 2002. *Icons of Evolution*. Washington, DC: Regnery Publishing Inc., 68-71.
6. Darwin, C. 1872. *On the Origin of Species By Means of Natural Selection*, 6th ed. London: John Murray, 420. Emphasis added.
7. Gould, S. J. 2002. *The Structure of Evolutionary Theory*. Cambridge, MA: Belknap Press, 59.
8. Bejan, The evolution of airplanes.
9. Colossians 1:16.

9

The Fatal Flaws of Living Fossils

Summary

Evolution says that creatures constantly change as a result of natural selection. But "living fossils" contradict that prediction. These creatures have been around for supposedly millions of years, and yet they have remained the same. One of the most famous "living fossils" is the coelacanth. It was found off the coast of South Africa in 1938. It blew evolutionary expectations. Since then, many other "living fossils" have been found, challenging the idea that creatures change and evolve over time. It seems that, far more often, they stay their well-designed selves.

Judy Rivers was stuck living out of her car for months. She was not poor—her bank accounts had $80,000. Yet she couldn't rent an apartment or access her money. The police even took her to jail once as an identity thief for using her own debit card.

Judy's problems all started one day when she woke up

"dead." Her name had somehow appeared on the Social Security Administration's Death Master File. Judy's story was told by CBS News' *60 Minutes* correspondent Scott Pelley, who quipped, "God may judge the quick and the dead but it's the states that collect the data."[1]

Pelley reported that being alive but mistaken for dead is "deadly serious business because when you're added to the file, that means that banks, the IRS, Medicare, law enforcement and the like, scratch you out of existence. But we found that the Death Master File is often fatally flawed."[1] Judy learned that getting off the Death Master File was harder than getting on. Worse yet, since she was living but officially considered dead, in evolutionary terms she was like a living fossil—a creature considered extinct that suddenly turns up alive.

Living Fossils: Fixing a Problem of Too Much Time

Judy had her problems, but living fossils cause their own troubles for evolutionists. In his review of a new book about such creatures, science writer Colin Barras observed "that peculiarly oxymoronic moniker, too, has survived—for around 150 years."[2] The term "living fossil," first used by Charles Darwin in his *Origin of Species*, does indeed sound like an oxymoron. However, it suits the way evolutionists apply it to their theory.

Their central problem is time—in this case, too much of it. If evolution is all about creatures changing over time, then how do evolutionists account for the many groups of creatures that, in the broad sense, did not change? The time involved in these cases is not trivial. In their way of thinking, you shouldn't be able to compare a 400-million-year-old fossil fish to its living counterpart and find no major differences.

Time can be an evolutionist's ally. Darwin appealed to incomprehensibly vast eons to smother any mental reservations about the impossibility of one kind of organism evolving into fundamentally different kinds. His thinking goes like this: If organisms have an enormous number of chances to change over eons, by sheer luck the seemingly impossible just may happen. But vast eras of time may also be an enemy to his theory. Why have horseshoe crabs changed hardly at all in 450 million years when fish, amphibians, reptiles, and mammals all supposedly emerged in succession in 550 million years from some "primitive" organism? Is this non-evolution (called *stasis*) of horseshoe crabs really the norm for all of life, or are creatures like them simply evolutionary anomalies?

Darwin assumed that static creatures like horseshoe crabs were deviations from the normal evolutionary processes. "These anomalous forms may be called living fossils; they have endured to the present day, from having inhabited a confined area, and from having been exposed to less varied, and therefore less severe, competition."[3] Is Darwin's assumption reasonable about less varied or severe conditions resulting in uniformity over hundreds of millions of years? His explanation may sound like an observation from nature, but it is really an imaginary conjecture. After all, these non-evolving creatures supposedly faced the same bleak multiple mass-extinction events that annihilated many others.

Barras offers another explanation, but since it lacks a scientific foundation he also turns to luck. "The fossil record suggests that every so often evolution hits the jackpot: an organism so impeccably and robustly suited to its environment that further modification is apparently unnecessary." After all, no one knows for sure "what singles out an organism as a survivor-in-waiting."[4] It seems that both his and Darwin's scenarios incline toward pure imagination.

Without a doubt, the term "living fossil" is a device intended to rescue evolutionary theory from the too-much-time dilemma by suggesting that organisms survive for eons without change because they live under less varied competition or are simply lucky. Just like the mental constructs used for Piltdown Man and "whale hips,"[5] the fatally flawed notion of living fossils leads to blunder upon blunder—some minor and others with major conceptual problems.

A Fish Mistakenly Added to Nature's Death Master File

Just as Judy Rivers was mistaken for dead, *National Geographic* recalls how "the primitive-looking coelacanth…was thought to have gone extinct with the dinosaurs 65 million years ago. But its discovery in 1938 by a South African museum curator on a local fishing trawler fascinated the world."[6] PBS's *NOVA* program on the subject, titled "Ancient Creature of the Deep," describes the coelacanth as "a bizarre fish and 'living fossil' that has changed little in its 400 million years on Earth."[7]

The coelacanth's discoverer, Marjorie Courtenay-Latimer, was the astute curator of East London Museum in South Africa. She had made known to the local fishermen her desire to see unusual specimens. On December 22, 1938, she was summoned to the wharf, where she observed a very strange five-foot-long fish. The fascinating letter exchanges between her and Dr. J. L.

B. Smith, a chemistry professor and ichthyologist at Rhodes University in nearby Grahamstown, are archived on *NOVA*'s website. Courtenay-Latimer's initial drawing of the fish was good enough that Smith recognized its similarity to fossil coelacanths...but he was skeptical.

After studying samples of the fish's scales, Smith became convinced of the discovery. *NOVA* described his first encounter with the fish, which had been preserved by taxidermy.

It had been nearly two months since the fish had come ashore, but that only made Smith's initial sighting of it all the more miraculous. "Although I had come prepared, that first sight [of the fish] hit me like a white-hot blast and made me feel shaky and queer, my body tingled," he wrote in Old Fourlegs. "I stood as if stricken to stone. Yes, there was not a shadow of doubt, scale by scale, bone by bone, fin by fin, it was a true Coelacanth."[8]

Evidently, scientists themselves can have strong emotional attachments to their worldviews. The evolutionary worldview may capture one's mind, in which case obvious questions can go unasked. How did this fish remain unchanged for hundreds of millions of years while other fish were allegedly changing to different kinds all around it? Since no one has an answer for "what singles out an organism as a survivor-in-waiting," is this kind of fish truly that ancient? The mistake of declaring a fish dead that really wasn't is not itself a major error. Evolutionists, however, commit an enormous scientific blunder by fabricating oxymoronic "living fossil" or "survivor in waiting" rescuing devices to save their theories.

Thought to have been long extinct, a museum curator discovered this coelacanth "living fossil" in 1938.

Imagining "Primitive" Features

In an evolutionary context, a primitive characteristic is one at an early stage of evolutionary development. There are temporal and usually qualitative dimensions evolutionists use to indicate that a primitive trait is early and less advanced. But there are problems with this approach.

If you started from an evolutionary perspective and carefully examined your face, then which features would you label as primitive? What scientific test would be capable of giving such a result? Actually, evolutionists usually accomplish this feat by just looking at a trait or DNA sequence and declaring, "That's primitive."

You could ask, What is the opposite of primitive? Is there a non-arbitrary standard by which one draws the line between the two? Tasks like that are not so clear, as Adrian Bejan correctly observes: "In biology, evolution is largely a mental construct built on imagination, because the time scale of animal evolution is immense relative to the time available to us for observations."[9] Could evolutionary blunders be based on mistaken mental visualizations of primordial features, or primitive life forms, or ancient epochs of life?

Darwin invented the term *living fossils* to explain the anomaly of creatures that had not evolved over supposed eons of time. Taking that assumption as fact, he claimed that living fossils also help us visualize primeval organisms: "Species and groups of species which are called aberrant [showing little evolutionary change], and which may fancifully be called living fossils, will aid us in forming a picture of the ancient forms of life."[10] Darwin's fanciful phrase actually expressed an evolutionary concept for framing life's history.

Commenting on the impact of the phrase, one writer concludes:

> It quickly multiplied in both academic writing and the popular press. Eventually, it came to signify creatures that had emerged long ago and had not changed for eons, preserving a primitive appearance unlike any other living thing. "Living fossil" was no longer a passing phrase; it had become a powerful concept shaping scientists' attitudes toward modern species. If certain creatures were frozen in evolutionary time, the reasoning went, then they could be our windows to ancient epochs of life.[11]

In 2011, evolutionary biologists studied "a newly discovered eel that inhabits an undersea cave in the Pacific Ocean [that] has been dubbed a 'living fossil' because of its primitive features."[12] What's even more remarkable about this living eel is that these evolutionists claim it is the most primitive eel in Earth's history, has been evolving independently from other eels for ages, and is a living fossil even though there are *no known* fossils of it. The original paper states, "Additional morphological and molecular analyses demonstrate that in some features it is more primitive than Recent eels, and in others, even more primitive than the oldest known fossil eels, suggesting that it represents a 'living fossil' without a known fossil record."[13] Coelacanth and this eel are only observed living in today's world. Evolutionists summon extraordinary imaginative skills enabling them to see primitive features in them and visualize their ancient environments. Those visualizations are subsequently published in science journals as if they are reality.

Other major evolutionary presumptions such as co-evolution, co-option, nature exercising agency, and convergent evolution duplicate the "primitive features" blunder. These are not *observations* of test results but are actually *declarations* based on fertile imaginations. One must ask, how much of the evolutionary scenario exists only in an evolutionist's mind…but not in reality?

Fossils and Living Counterparts Look Similarly Designed

Creationist Carl Werner compiled the most complete photo record of what evolutionists label as living fossils.[14] His fascinating work covers all major animal phyla living today. Included are many "modern" mammals found in rock layers dating back to the "dinosaur era." Over 21 different animal and plant types show essentially no change between their fossils and living counterparts—even though evolutionists tag them with different genus or species names to line up with their assumptions. Non-evolution, or *stasis*, seems to be the reality for all of life.

Creationists expect that fossils of living creatures will look like what we observe today since the ideas of "ancient" versus "modern" life are arbitrary mental fabrications. Given the fossil/living counterpart similarity, why couldn't the fossil's age actually be closer to its contemporary counterpart's?

We can appreciate Judy Rivers and the coelacanth for who and what they really are now that they're off the Death Master File. Yet a mind can become conditioned to still see "the primitive-looking coelacanth," but only by overlooking its elegant design—such as how eight powerful fins give it remarkable maneuverability, or enable it to swim belly up or remain motionless while head down. Or dismissing how the photodetector cells in its large eyes are sensitive enough to detect a single photon of light while swimming down to depths of over 1,500 feet. But for those fixed in reality, these sophisticated designs of a "primitive" fish clearly show that "the works of the Lord are great, studied by all who have pleasure in them" (Psalm 111:2).

References

1. Dead or Alive. *60 Minutes*. Aired March 15, 2015, rebroadcast February 28, 2016.
2. Barras, C. 2011. The species that evaded extinction. *New Scientist*. 211 (2829): 50-51.
3. Darwin, C. 1872. *On the Origin of Species by Means of Natural Selection*, 6th ed. London: John Murray, 83.
4. Barras, The species that evaded extinction.
5. Guliuzza, R. 2015. Major Evolutionary Blunders: The Imaginary Piltdown Man. *Acts & Facts*. 44 (12): 12-14; and Guliuzza, R. 2016. Major Evolutionary Blunders: Are Whales and Evolution Joined at the Hip? *Acts & Facts*. 45 (3): 12-14.
6. Coelacanth. *National Geographic*. Posted on animals.nationalgeographic.com.
7. Ancient Creature of the Deep. *NOVA*. Posted on pbs.org.
8. Tyson, P. Moment of Discovery. *NOVA*. Posted on pbs.org.

9. Bejan, A., J. D. Charles, and S. Lorente. 2014. The evolution of airplanes. *Journal of Applied Physics.* 116 (4): 044901.

10. Darwin, *On the Origin of Species*, 427.

11. Jabr, F. The Rise and Fall of the Living Fossil. *Nautilus.* Posted on nautil.us March 19, 2015.

12. Rincon, P. New Pacific eel is a 'living fossil', scientists say. *BBC News.* Posted on bbc.com August 17, 2011, accessed March 11, 2016.

13. Johnson, G. D. et al. A 'living fossil' eel (Anguilliformes: Protoanguillidae, fam. nov.) from an undersea cave in Palau. *Proceedings of the Royal Society B.* Published online August 17, 2011.

14. Werner, C. 2009. *Living Fossils.* Green Forest, AR: New Leaf Press.

10

Breaking Dollo's Law

Summary

Evolutionist Louis Dollo said, "An organism cannot return, even partially, to a previous state already realized in its ancestral series." Today, this is known as *Dollo's law*. It was based upon the statistical improbability that an organism would "re-evolve" something that its ancestors had. But, as usual, that evolutionary prediction failed. Many creatures are found with features that their "ancestors" had and lost. One example is mandibular teeth that "re-appeared" in frogs after supposedly being absent in their lineage for 220 million years. One evolutionist said, "There is no support for the model of irreversible evolution (Dollo's law)." According to a creationist worldview, it's possible that creatures were created to self-adjust to their environments, which could mean reappearing traits, or "re-evolving" in evolutionary terms. The continual violation of Dollo's law exemplifies another failed evolutionary prediction.

According to the brilliant conception of the immortal Charles Darwin (1809-1882): Evolution—the transformation of organisms—results from the fixation of useful individual variations provoked by the struggle for existence under the influence of natural selection. All species—animal or plant—which exist or have existed since the appearance of life on earth, must originate via this fundamental law.[1]

So began "The Laws of Evolution" published in 1893 by Louis Dollo, curator of Belgium's Royal Museum of Natural History. Dollo was a renowned Belgian paleontologist who gained his reputation for his work on *Iguanodon* dinosaurs and the rules he formulated for paleobiology, the study of the biology of fossil life forms.

Interestingly, Harvard University's eminent paleontologist Stephen Gould contributed to the publishing of Louis Dollo's *Papers on Paleontology and Evolution* in 1980, a date that coincides with the period of considerable debate about Gould's punctuated equilibrium mechanism of evolution. Dollo's first law of evolution was "that evolution occurred by abrupt leaps,"[1] which was also one premise of Gould's mechanism. Dollo actually proposed three laws based on his field observations that have been influential in framing evolutionary research and theory. He is remembered today for his second law, which bears his name.

Dollo's Law of Irreversibility

Dollo stated "that an organism cannot return, even partially, to a previous state already realized in its ancestral series."[1] Today, this is known as Dollo's law of irreversibility. Accordingly, most evolutionists believe that evolution simply proceeds forward. For organisms with a membrane-bound nucleus, they hold that the operation of natural processes is sufficient to account for the diversity of the organisms' genes and traits. They believe there is no specific course that evolution is ordained to follow, but once it proceeds, there is essentially no "reverse evolution."

Paleontological discoveries and theory have not remained static since Dollo formulated his law. The principle of irreversibility has nevertheless been preserved, though interpretations of findings underlying Dollo's law have changed and the rationale for it has been modified. Those currently believing in irreversibility do not appeal to an abundance of observations. Rather, the belief is justified by the mathematical improbability of a single evolving lineage proceeding and then reversing along the same path. Richard Dawkins notes,

"Dollo's Law" states that evolution is irreversible....Dollo's Law is really just a statement about the statistical improbability of following exactly the same evolutionary trajectory twice (or, indeed, any particular trajectory), in either direction.[2]

Gould agrees with this understanding. He says,

Thus, for example, Dollo's law of irreversibility...only restates the general principles of mathematical probability for the specific case of temporal changes based on large numbers of relatively independent components.[3]

Of course, if re-evolution is prohibited by the exceedingly low probability of a blind process acting on random mutations in this manner, then one could ask why such claims wouldn't also apply to evolution itself.

Does Dollo's law deserve the status of scientific law? "Scientific law" conveys a very high level of confidence that the principle(s) embodied in the law accurately conform to reality. The status of being called a scientific law is obtained after repeated observations and experiments consistently confirm its principles. True laws are so consistent that any violation of them would constitute a miracle. If Dollo's law is repeatedly violated, then that would constitute a major mistake in evolutionary theory. And it would be a blunder that has been reiterated in evolutionary education for decades.

Dollo's Blunder: Traits Do Reappear

If organisms break scientific laws, then it is the law that needs a trial, not the organism. Several researchers have conducted that trial. One evolutionary biologist stated, "Recent phylogenetic studies have revealed several potential examples in which Dollo's law seems to be violated, where lost structures appear to have been regained over evolutionary time." He found mandibular teeth in one lineage of frogs that re-appeared after being lost, he believes, for about 220 million years. He claims this "shows that there is no support for the model of irreversible evolution (Dollo's law)."[4]

Several 2016 papers deal with evolutionary reversals contrary to Dollo. "Single evolutionary reversals occur when a character changes from an ancestral state to a derived state and then back to the ancestral state within a single lineage," reports University of Hawaii researchers in a study on a native bird species' beak length. "Multiple reversals extend the process by returning to the derived or ancestral state several times within a single lineage." The team documents "three single and two multiple reversals of bill length on six main islands from oldest to youngest, consistent with the phylogeny of the lineage."[5]

Two other evolutionists hope to treat drug-resistant malaria through various paths of "reverse evolution" back to a susceptible state. Their frustration with Dollo's law spilled over:

The lack of a coherent understanding of reverse evolution is partly due to conceptual ambiguity: the term 'reverse evolution' is misleading, as it implies directionality in a process (Darwinian evolution) that is near-sighted and agnostic with regard to goal. This has spawned similarly dubious concepts, such as Dollo's Law, asserting that evolution is intrinsically irreversible.[6]

Recently, a study documented "loss and reversals" of a molar tooth crest in a lineage of extinct kangaroos after a time gap believed to be 15 million years.[7] How can this happen? "We found that contrary to Dollo's law in biology, features lost in evolution can re-evolve when evolution 'tinkers' with the way features are assembled in the embryo," reported co-researcher Aidan Couzens of Flinders University.[8] The report continues how "the researchers argue that 'reanimating genetically mothballed features may be "allowed" by evolution when it aligns with pressures that determine an animal's ecology.'" Other true instances of "reverse evolution" may have been missed previously since "biologists have often discounted the potential for evolution to shift into reverse, dismissing such occurrences as convergent evolution, 'where similar features evolve independently in organisms that are not closely related.'"[8]

Scientifically pliable invocations of evolution "allowing" or "tinkering with" things, coupled with the mental construct of "convergent evolution" and unquantified "ecological pressures," place Dollo's law squarely in the mystical realm surrounding evolutionary explanations. Which explains why anyone doing an internet survey discovers violations of Dollo's law, including reversals for wings in stick insects, coiling in snail shells, color vision, eggshells in boid snakes, and many more.

However, some scientists criticize findings that question Dollo's law. They defend Dollo by asserting that their phylogenetic trees are superior to "the moderate level of robustness of many phylogenies" in critical studies.[9] One researcher allows some latitude for Dollo's mistake but not for its continued perpetuation. He implies that Dollo made a valid law but not in the sense of criminal law. Rather, it is more akin to tax law because it has some "loopholes." Yet, he asserts that the theoretical work of Dollo's present defenders may have "devastating flaws" of its own.[10]

An evolutionary law that is violated constitutes a major evolutionary blunder. Possibly Dollo only made a minor blunder in mislabeling an inference as a law, but his overstated and under-supported conjecture misled research for decades. Also, as soon as striking evidences of "re-evolution" were discovered, repeated salvage efforts like classifying them as merely loopholes hinder scientific progress. For example, since Dollo's law was one element of evolutionary theory that actually was predictive (i.e., that re-evolution would not be observed), when observations showed that the prediction was faulty, pursuing non-evolutionary explanations would be sensible—but frequently has not been done.

Overlooking Design-Based Explanations

Perhaps reappearing traits may *not* be a violation of any law. Nor are they improbability-conquering miracles. This phenomenon is feasibly the outworking of an ingenious design for the purpose of enabling creatures to continually "fill the earth" (Genesis 1:28).

One study on owl monkeys correctly notes that if organisms become too specialized to a niche, then this could "lead to a genetic constraint on adaptation if the environment subsequently changes."[11] In other words, specialization could force organisms down an unrecoverable one-way street. How might human engineers address this issue? For some uses, they may design an entity to stay constrained. In contrast, they may also design mechanisms within self-adjusting entities to turn off in order to go one direction and turn back on to reverse direction. That entity could escape a one-way specialization trap—especially if a trap was assured to happen repeatedly. Do organisms display this turn-off/turn-on characteristic?

Researchers found that after the loss of a structure, in many cases "the genetic and developmental architecture to develop such structures continues to be fully present."[12] Couzens also reviewed how reversibility may be variably widespread among organisms:

It has been argued that trait reversibility may be promoted when there is reutilization of conserved developmental pathways...[and] the reutilization of regulatory pathways and constituent genes is widespread in development...and ancestral states are recoverable across a diverse spectrum of metazoan structures.[13]

So, many organisms do have mechanisms to allow recovery of ancestral states. These mechanisms remain in place, but they can be deactivated for generations and then reactivated and accessed during embryonic development in other generations. What can explain the persistence of this underlying "developmental architecture" that "reanimates genetically mothballed features"?

Evolutionists claim that the information is conserved. "Conserved" is the evolution-speak label tagged to the phenomenon of finding nearly identical traits across *many* wildly different organisms. Such organisms supposedly "emerged" from unrelated pathways and carried unchanged (i.e., conserved) information for the similar trait across evolutionary time—while many other traits were greatly changing. Finding information for similar traits is certainly a factual observation. But believing that they are "conserved" is a declaration based in imagination…and firm convictions that evolution happened. In contrast, if the common trait is found in only a few diverse creatures, then evolutionists imagine convergent evolution.

There is a less-mystical, more-straightforward explanation that is consistent with what engineers do. It may be that different creatures are designed to retain specific developmental architecture for the common purpose of reutilizing regulatory pathways to recover ancestral states when the situation for them is suitable. Stable mechanisms that can be reactivated when useful are more consistent with intelligent forethought since "Darwinian evolution…is near-sighted and agnostic with regard to goal."[14] This may be just one of many incredibly complex innate mechanisms that enable organisms to match their traits to dynamic environmental conditions so they can continually fulfill their God-given mandate to be fruitful, multiply, and fill seas, sky, and Earth (Genesis 1:22, 28).

References

1. Dollo, L. 1893. The Laws of Evolution. Extract from the *Bulletin de la Société Belge de Géologie de Paléontologie & D'Hydrologie.* 7: 164-166. Emphasis in original.
2. Dawkins, R. 1986. *The Blind Watchmaker.* New York: W. W. Norton & Company, 94. Emphasis in original.
3. Gould, S. J. 2002. *The Structure of Evolutionary Theory.* Cambridge, MA: Harvard University Press, 901-902.
4. Wiens, J. J. 2011. Re-evolution of lost mandibular teeth in frogs after more than 200 million years, and re-evaluating Dollo's Law. *Evolution.* 65 (5): 1283-1296.
5. Freed, L. A., M. C. I. Medeiros, and R. L. Cann. 2016. Multiple Reversals of Bill Length over 1.7 Million Years in a Hawaiian Bird Lineage. *The American Naturalist.* 187 (3): 363-371.
6. Ogbunugafor, C. B. and D. Hartl. 2016. A pivot mutation impedes reverse evolution across an adaptive landscape for drug resistance in Plasmodium vivax. *Malaria Journal.* 15: 40.
7. Couzens, A. M. C. et al. 2016. The role of inhibitory dynamics in the loss and reemergence of macropodoid tooth traits. *Evolution.* 70 (3): 568-585.
8. Kangaroos chew over evolutionary theory. Flinders University news release. Posted on blogs. flinders.edu.au April 18, 2016, accessed April 26, 2016.
9. Galis, F., J. W. Arntzen, and R. Lande. 2010. Dollo's Law and the irreversibility of digit loss in Bachia. *Evolution.* 64 (8): 2466-2476.
10. Wiens, Re-evolution of lost mandibular teeth in frogs, 1292.
11. Mundy, N. I. et al. 2016. Can colour vision re-evolve? Variation in the X-linked opsin locus of cathemeral Azara's owl monkeys (Aotus azarae azarae). *Frontiers in Zoology.* 13 (1): 9.
12. Galis, Dollo's Law, 2466.
13. Couzens, The role of inhibitory dynamics, 568. Emphasis added.
14. Ogbunugafor, A pivot mutation impedes reverse evolution.

11

The "Degenerate" Genetic Code?

Summary

Evolutionists habitually shift definitions to suit their ideology. Such is the case with *degeneracy.* Flowing out of their assumption that creatures are full of useless features from random mutations, evolutionists quickly labeled some of the DNA code for the building blocks of proteins as "degenerate"—that is, they were superfluous or redundant. However, as new evidence is uncovered, "degenerate" DNA turns out to be enormously functional. But rather than admit error, evolutionists simply redefine their terms. Suddenly, "degenerate" means "to perform function"! Even in the face of repeated refutation, evolutionists refuse to admit the failures of their theory. They just shift definitions.

"Newspeak" was the language developed by the fictional totalitarian regime Oceania in George Orwell's classic novel *1984.* The regime redefined words and slogans as a means of thought control over its citizens. Often, Newspeak words meant the exact opposite of the "Oldspeak" vocabulary. Citizens' thinking eventually became characterized by contradictory beliefs that were embraced simultaneously, a practice known as "doublethink." For instance, the Ministry of Truth produced Newspeak and fabricated history-altering propaganda. And in the Ministry of Love, people were tortured for committing "thoughtcrimes" such as individualism and independent thinking. Orwell's novel cautions us against being fooled by cunning misapplication of words or deceptive redefinitions.

Does Degenerate Mean Degraded or Upgraded?

The answer to this question may seem obvious. Obvious, that is, if you think in Oldspeak, but elusive if you think in Evolutionspeak. When evolutionists claim that a biological feature is degenerate, do they mean that it is degraded, superfluous, redundant, or a defining characteristic of biological complexity? Apparently, it means any of these, depending on the evolutionist and the particular conclusions he or she is trying to draw.

A research paper from the 1970s described the genetic code as "a universal, highly degenerate, three-letter code."[1] For reference, a three-letter code, also called a *codon*, is a group of three bases of DNA that specify a single amino-acid building block for a protein. DNA bases are also referred to as *nucleotides*.

Exploring the evolution of genes, a more recent paper states, "Because there are much more different codons than coded amino acids, the genetic code is called degenerate. Since the discovery of the genetic code...how it is degenerated is one of the most fascinating problems of genetics." This fascinating problem has evolutionary implications: "The hypotheses trying to explain the evolution of the genetic code can be divided into two groups [mechanistic and random]."[2] The authors advocate the random hypothesis and describe how the alleged evolution and degeneracy of the genetic code developed together.

What might a biology undergraduate student make of these characterizations of genetic degeneracy? Evolutionists believe that genetic variety is mindlessly fractionated between organisms in a deadly struggle for life. Destruction associated with a struggle for life may fit the primary definition of "degenerate" in dictionaries like *Merriam-Webster:*

1.a: having declined or become less specialized (as in nature, character, structure, or function) from an ancestral or former state; b: having sunk to a condition below that which is normal to a type; especially: having sunk to a lower and usually corrupt and vicious state; c: degraded.[3]

Therefore, the student could readily interpret genomic degeneracy according to its common meaning—degradation.

But the student may be pushed to another evolutionary meaning of degenerate. Because there are more codons than coded amino acids, degeneracy might support evolution if some of the codons (or one of the three nucleotides making a codon) were superfluous. This understanding aligns with reports claiming that one in 200 human genes is "nonsense." A lead researcher stated, "Our study suggests that overall, gene loss has not been a major evolutionary force: our genome does not seem to be in a hurry to get rid of these 'superfluous' genes."[4] Since living things supposedly evolve through the inefficient survival-of-the-fittest process, degeneracy could result from

DNA being "cobbled together"[5] through "evolution as a 'tinkerer,' building new machines from salvaged parts."[6] Therefore, junk DNA is declared as evidence of evolution…and certainly not indicators of good design.

As the student gathers yet more background information on the evolution of the genetic code, he may be surprised that in yet another report degeneracy does not mean superfluous, or functionally redundant, or degraded, but actually "degeneracy is a ubiquitous biological property" that researchers argue "is a feature of *complexity* at genetic, cellular, system, and population levels."[7] This novel evolutionary-based usage affirms,

Degeneracy, the ability of elements that are structurally different to perform the same function or yield the same output…is both necessary for, and an inevitable outcome of, natural selection.[7]

It seems that evolutionists can invoke degeneracy to bolster their favored concept.

To find a way through all of the Evolutionspeak on genomic degeneracy, the student can turn to actual studies of function for the three nucleotides in a codon. These studies point to another major evolutionary blunder since *all* of these possible evolutionary understandings of degeneracy are not supported by the science.

In Evolutionspeak, Degeneracy Is Stunningly Wrong

A detailed literature review in 2014 found that even if different codons prescribed the same amino acid in a protein, the codon differences still mattered in how the protein was made.

The final folding shape of proteins is vital to their function. David D'Onofrio and David Abel documented that the DNA and its corresponding RNA sequence carried information not only for the proper amino acid sequence but also to control the *timing* of its folding. They "demonstrate that this TP [translational pausing] code is programmed into the supposedly degenerate redundancy of the codon table."[8] What this means is that the code of differing codons, even if they specify the same amino acid, still supplies important information, information that "purposely slows or speeds up the translation-decoding process....Variable translation rates help prescribe functional folding of the nascent protein. Redundancy of the codon to amino acid mapping, therefore, is anything but superfluous or degenerate."[8]

A recent experiment again shows that the specific nucleotides in a codon do matter. Mutations to a codon that do not change the protein-coding sequence are called *synonymous.* The consensus view was, "Until recently, most biologists believed that so-called silent mutations, created by 'synonymous' DNA changes—those that do not affect the protein-coding sequence—had very weak effects on the evolution of organisms." But this long-term experiment with bacteria found "that single highly beneficial synonymous mutations can allow organisms to rapidly evolve and adapt to their environment."[9] Another "interesting phenomenon" was that bacteria with different codons initially, when faced with the same challenges, seemed to converge on the same changes. Researchers found that "furthermore, these mutations occurred at single points within the gene, were highly beneficial, and they seemed to recur in multiple experiments."[9]

A nucleotide order that specifies rapid, repeatable, and useful adjustments to changed conditions does not sound like the serendipitous side effect of random "silent mutations" but rather speaks loudly of the designed outcome of intentional planning. The genomic code is not degraded or superfluous. It is also clear that structurally different elements that specify a common element do not necessarily yield the same output. Observations like these prompted D'Onofrio and Abel to conclude, "The functionality of condonic [sic] redundancy denies the ill-advised label of 'degeneracy.'"[10]

Corollaries to the "Degenerate Genome" Blunder

Commenting on wide-ranging ramifications of D'Onofrio and Abel's work, Casey Luskin made an insightful observation regarding how it relates to the conclusions of many other evolutionary studies. He observes,

Seeking to infer the activity of natural selection, evolutionary biologists statistically analyze the frequency of synonymous (thought to be functionally unimportant) and nonsynonymous (thought to be functionally important) codons in a gene....As the thinking goes, if synonymous codons are functionally unimportant, then three conclusions may follow: a bias toward synonymous codons implies purifying selection in the gene, a bias towards nonsynonymous codons implies positive selection, and an equal balance implies neutral evolution (no selection). But if synonymous codons can have important functional meaning, then the whole methodology goes out the window, and hundreds of studies that used these methods to infer "selection" during the supposed "evolution of genes" could be wrong.[11]

Aside from the science showing that the genome is not degenerate in any evolutionary sense, there is another—more important—lesson made evident by this blunder. It pertains to Evolutionspeak within evolutionary literature. This lesson flows from the ambiguous usage of words that oppose their primary meaning. That is conceptually misleading, and it's possible that this Evolutionspeak could produce the same effect as Newspeak. Orwell was concerned about misleading definitions used by powerful institutions to impose big lies on those under their control. He illustrated this in *1984* with the Party's oft-repeated mantra "war is peace, ignorance is strength, freedom is slavery."

In scientific literature, metaphors, analogies, and anthropomorphisms abound. Some are useful in bringing clarity. However, cross-definitions, false analogies, or applying a word to something that its definition could never support can be misleading. This practice is highly detrimental to science, which is structured on precise language and clarity. We must be on guard to make sure Evolutionspeak doesn't creep into our own way of thinking about science.

The Genetic Code Is a Design Marvel

As noted above, *repeatability* is found in synonymous changes enabling bacteria to consistently overcome challenges. Repeatability is not a hallmark of chance outcomes but is suggestive that this result is due to designed mechanisms.

It is also telling how Gerald Edelman and Joseph Gally recognize that backup, or functionally redundant, systems are indicative of design. However, their worldview not only precludes any consideration of that conclusion but also shapes their choice of vocabulary in conveying their thoughts to others—i.e., Evolutionspeak. They astutely note:

The contrast between degeneracy and redundancy at the structural level is sharpened by comparing design and selection in engineering and evolution, respectively. In engineering systems, logic prevails, and, for fail-safe operation, redundancy is built into design. This is not the case for biological systems. Indeed, not the least of Darwin's achievements was to lay the argument by design to rest.[12]

Thus, they believe "the term 'degeneracy' is more apt than 'functional redundancy.'"[12]

When humans can identify the true source of fail-safe redundancy, it is always an indicator of good design and a good designer. Given that, redundancy of a code embedded in another code reveals great design. D'Onofrio explains, "Redundancy in the primary genetic code allows for additional independent codes….We have shown a secondary code superimposed upon the primary codonic prescription of amino acid sequence in proteins."[13]

Geneticist Dr. Jeffrey Tomkins of the Institute for Creation Research summarizes that "we are only beginning to decipher the true complexity of these different genetic languages," but we do know that "for the genome to function in all its complexity, many different codes and languages are used, and they all mesh and work interactively with one another….These highly complex language systems speak directly to a Creator of infinite wisdom and capabilities."[14] How true. For by the Lord Jesus "all things were created that are in heaven and that are on earth, visible and invisible" (Colossians 1:16).

References

1. Lagerkvist, U. 1978. "Two out of three": An alternate method for codon reading. *Proceedings of the National Academy of Sciences.* 75 (4): 1759-1762.
2. Dudkiewicz, M. et al. 2005. Correspondence between mutation and selection pressure and the genetic code degeneracy in the gene evolution. *Future Generation Computer Systems.* 21 (7): 1033-1039.
3. Degenerate. *Merriam-Webster* online. Posted on merriam-webster.com.
4. The nonsense in our genes: One in 200 genes superfluous? Wellcome Trust Sanger Institute press release, February 5, 2009.
5. Guliuzza, R. J. 2016. Major Evolutionary Blunders: The "Poor Design" of Our Recurrent Laryngeal Nerve. *Acts & Facts.* 45 (4): 17-19.
6. Clements, A. et al. 2009. The reducible complexity of a mitochondrial molecular machine. *Proceedings of the National Academy of Sciences.* 106 (37): 15791-15795.
7. Edelman, G. M. and J. A. Gally. 2001. Degeneracy and complexity in biological systems. *Proceedings of the National Academy of Sciences.* 98 (24): 13763-13768. Emphasis added.
8. D'Onofrio, D. J. and D. L. Abel. 2014. Redundancy of the genetic code enables translational pausing. *Frontiers in Genetics.* 5 (140): 1-16.
9. Caspermeyer, J. 2016. When Silent Mutations Provide Evolutionary Advantages. *Molecular Biology and Evolution.* 33 (6): 1639.
10. D'Onofrio, Redundancy of the genetic code, 13.
11. Luskin, C. Paper Finds Functional Reasons For "Redundant" Codons, Fulfilling a Prediction from Intelligent Design. *Evolution News and Views.* Posted on evolutionnews.org August 25, 2014, accessed June 2, 2016.
12. Edelman, Degeneracy and complexity in biological systems, 13763.
13. D'Onofrio, Redundancy of the genetic code, 13.
14. Tomkins, J. P. 2015. Extreme Information: Biocomplexity of Interlocking Genome Languages. *Creation Research Society Quarterly.* 51 (3): 186-201.

12

The Imaginary *Archaeoraptor*

Summary

Evolutionists have a tendency to jump to conclusions and claim a fossil as evidence that is later revealed to be a hoax. Such is the case with the infamous *Archaeoraptor*. In 1999, *National Geographic* splashed its discovery all over the world, hailing it as "a true missing link in the complex chain that connects dinosaurs to birds." However, within months, paleontologists discovered that it was the upper body of a bird literally glued to the legs and tail of a dinosaur. This was one of the many times fossil forgery found its way into evolutionary theory, being helped along by the wild imaginations of paleontologists. We must be careful not to let imagination get the best of us. Rather, we should see things as they are.

The Federal Aviation Administration (FAA) is quite serious about flying safety. If an aircraft crashes, the FAA will conduct an investigation called a Root Cause Analysis. This involves methodical detective work that tracks events from the moment of the crash back in time. Flight and voice data recorders are invaluable to the inquiry. Root Cause Analysis identifies the most obvious problem that led to the crash and then lists the problem's cause. That cause is then treated like a problem in itself, and the cause for its occurrence is investigated. This cycle is repeated until the very first cause is discovered. Finding that initial problem, the root cause, helps prevent similar crashes in the future.

It would seem completely irrational if these problems weren't fixed in future airplanes and were somehow accepted as just a fact of flying. Amazingly, evolutionary theory tolerates a built-in root-cause problem: fossil forgery.

One frustrated evolutionary paleontologist vented his feelings after a highly publicized "missing link" was exposed as yet another hoax.

Red-faced and downhearted, paleontologists are growing convinced that they have been snookered by a bit of fossil fakery from China. The "feathered dinosaur" specimen that they recently unveiled to much fanfare apparently combines the tail of a dinosaur with the body of a bird, they say. "It's the craziest thing I've ever been involved with in my career," says paleontologist Philip J. Currie of the Royal Tyrrell Museum of Paleontology in Drumheller, Alberta.[1]

Currie is referring to an embarrassing major evolutionary blunder linked to a fossil forgery. This time it involved *Archaeoraptor liaoningensis* ("ancient bird of prey from Liaoning"), featured in the 1999 *National Geographic* article "Feathers for *T.*

rex?"[2] After this fraudulent fossil was exposed, commentators pointed out similarities with the notorious Piltdown Man hoax.[3]

Two Fossils Equal One *Archaeoraptor*

Scientists still don't know how the *Archaeoraptor* specimen was smuggled out of China and ended up in the United States. We do know that in 1998 Stephen Czerkas, curator of the Dinosaur Museum in Utah, purchased it for the tidy sum of $80,000. Czerkas labored with Xu Xing of China's prestigious Institute of Vertebrate Paleontology and Palcoanthropology and Phillip Currie to study the specimen. The National Geographic Society sponsored the project.

Archaeoraptor's debut was accomplished with widespread publicity. *National Geographic*'s November 1999 press release used language remarkably similar to other fossil forgeries—such as the 1913 description of Piltdown Man and the 2009 description of Ida, a lemur-like animal thought to document human evolution.[3] In the *Archaeoraptor* press release, Czerkas states, "It's a missing link that has the advanced characters of birds and undeniable dinosaurian characters as well."[4]

The National Geographic Society has since pulled that press release from their website, but ICR geologist Steven Austin captured the release's salient points in a contemporaneous *Acts & Facts* article in 2000. He states,

> The turkey-sized animal according to *National Geographic* "…is a true missing link in the complex chain that connects dinosaurs to birds. It seems to capture the paleontological 'moment' when dinosaurs were becoming birds." According to their press release, the anatomy of *Archaeoraptor* proves a

feathered theropod dinosaur was capable of flight. The features include: "…a very advanced, birdlike shoulder structure, wishbone and big sternum—all indicating the animal was a powerful flier. Remains of feathers surround the specimen's bones. Yet its tail was strikingly similar to the stiff tails of a family of predatory dinosaurs known as dromaeosaurs, which includes the 'raptors' of *Jurassic Park*." Several remarkable characteristics are noted. "This mix of advanced and primitive features is exactly what scientists would expect to find in dinosaurs experimenting with flight," and, "It's a missing link between terrestrial dinosaurs and birds that could actually fly."[4]

Just like the Piltdown Man blunder, these evolutionists saw what they wanted to see. Unfortunately, their strong belief in dinosaur-to-bird evolution led to mental images that overcame the empirical data. A Chinese craftsman apparently made a fossil to match their imaginations!

Based on nothing more than a mental visualization of what they already believed, the *National Geographic* article made the definitive pronouncement, "We can now say that birds are theropods just as confidently as we say that humans are mammals. Everything from lunch boxes to museum exhibits will change to reflect this revelation."[5] But within months, paleontologists showed that *Archaeoraptor* was the upper body of a bird literally glued to the legs and tail of a dinosaur.[6]

Imagination and Evolution

It is enlightening to observe the rapid sequence of events surrounding *Archaeoraptor*. All of us can empathize with someone getting carried away with excitement. But how could a whole team of scientific researchers demonstrate a wholesale lack of cautious judgment?

Well, the root cause of evolution's continuing problem with far-flung conjectures is pretty basic: *imagination*. The late evolutionary theorist Stephen Jay Gould calls it *extrapolation* and says it is an essential element of evolutionary theory.

Gould writes that paleontologists use "a set of procedures for making strong inferences about phyletic [evolutionary] history from data of an imperfect record that cannot, in any case, 'see' past causes directly, but can only draw conclusions from preserved results of these causes." They explain the past through "large scale results by extrapolation from short-term processes...[and] extrapolation to longer times and effects of evolutionary changes actually observed in historic times (usually by analogy to domestication and horticulture)."[7]

Of course, the "longer times" that Gould envisions are enormous, as is the amount of imagination needed to fill the gaps. Thus, Charles Darwin unashamedly invoked imagination—as do leading evolutionists like Richard Dawkins and Jerry Coyne. Yet these scientists imply that creationists suffer from *far too little* scientific imagination.[3]

This helps explain how evolutionists can merely look at fossil bones and see "transitional" features, or look at an odd fish from the ocean depths and see "primitive" features. Since imagination is a fundamental element of evolutionary theory, the blunders that accompany it will continue.

National Geographic published a few details of how they were duped. They write,

The tail and hind limbs were identified in 2000 as belonging to a *Microraptor zhaoianus,* a small, bipedal, meat-eating dinosaur with some bird-like features...[while] the avian parts of the false dinosaur-bird fossil are from one specimen, a fish-eating bird known as *Yanornis martini....Yanornis* had advanced features approaching those of modern birds, and strong flying abilities.[8]

Imagination enables evolutionists to see both *Microraptor* and *Yanornis* somehow evolving into "modern" birds with "advanced" features. Unfortunately, the criteria for "primitive," "advanced," and so on reside only in imagination.

ICR Science Writer Brian Thomas recently documented that, in spite of Czerka's *Archaeoraptor* blunder, the cycle continues with other fossils.

In 2002, Czerkas and his wife self-published a book called *Feathered Dinosaurs and the Origin of Flight* in which they discussed *Scansoriopteryx* in context of dinosaur evolution into birds. His stance on *Archaeoraptor* as a real fossil did a complete flip-flop shortly after its exposure as a fraud, and now his stance on *Scansoriopteryx* as a dinosaur has reversed as well.[9]

On the same topic, Thomas also reports on some major anatomical barriers for dinosaur-to-bird evolution.[10]

Evolution Continues to Blunder

Obviously the FAA and evolutionists handle root cause problems quite differently. The root cause of being duped by fossil forgeries is the need for evolutionists to fill substantial time gaps with imagination. So, in spite of the fact that birds have only been observed to reproduce other birds, evolutionary imagination spawns an eternal optimism of finding a "missing link" that may make researchers gullible to forgeries. One evolutionary paleoanthropologist admitted, "We have only to recall the Piltdown adventure to see how easily susceptible researchers can be manipulated into believing that they have actually found just what they had been looking for."[11]

It's valid for a scientist to ask, "How much of the evolutionary story, from its evidence to its mechanism, is only an extrapolated mystical mental construct?" This question is also somewhat of a warning. Once these mental constructs take on a life of their own by getting swept into the day-to-day evolutionary rhetoric and literature, everyone dealing with these imaginary concepts may tend to begin treating them as if they were real.

References
1. Monastersky, R. 2000. All mixed up over birds and dinosaurs. *Science News*. 157 (3): 38.
2. Sloan, C. P. 1999. Feathers for *T. rex*? New birdlike fossils are missing links in dinosaur evolution. *National Geographic*. 196: 98-107.
3. Guliuzza, R. 2015. Major Evolutionary Blunders: The Imaginary Piltdown Man. *Acts & Facts*. 44 (12): 12-14.
4. Austin, S. A. 2000. *Archaeoraptor*: Feathered Dinosaur from National Geographic Doesn't Fly. *Acts & Facts*. 29 (3).
5. Sloan, Feathers for *T. rex*?, 102.
6. Mayell, H. Dino Hoax Was Mainly Made of Ancient Bird, Study Says. *National Geographic News*. Posted on news.nationalgeographic.com November 20, 2002, accessed July 4, 2016.
7. Gould, S. J. 2002. *The Structure of Evolutionary Theory*. Cambridge, MA: Harvard University Press, 59.
8. Mayell, Dino Hoax.
9. Thomas, B. Second Look Causes Scientist to Reverse Dino-Bird Claim. *Creation Science Update*. Posted on ICR.org July 18, 2014, accessed July 5, 2016.
10. Thomas, B. Fixed Bird Thigh Nixes Dino-to-bird Development. *Creation Science Update*. Posted on ICR.org June 22, 2009, accessed July 14, 2014.

11. Maienschein, J. 1997. The One and the Many: Epistemological Reflections on the Modern Human Origins Debates. In *Conceptual Issues in Modern Human Origins Research*. Clark, G. A. and C. M. Willermet, eds. Hawthorne, NY: Aldine de Gruyter, 413.

13

Evolutionists Can't See Eye Design

Summary

Darwin thought the eye was complex, but nothing evolution can't handle. Today, that sentiment remains. Evolutionists dismiss the complexity of the eye by simply pointing out what they think are flaws. For them, what they perceive as flaws and engineering mistakes within organisms is strong evidence that they were cobbled together through evolutionary trial-and-error. Evolutionist Francis Ayala says the eye has "deficiencies" that are "outright dysfunctional." However, like his evolutionary colleagues, he doesn't understand the basic biological function of what he is criticizing. Much mainstream research has been published that shows the eye was designed for optimal performance. There are no "deficiencies," only amazing engineering. As one research paper concludes, "The retina is revealed as an optimal structure designed for improving the sharpness of images." Everywhere we look, God's intelligence is clearly seen.

Ignorance and a limited perspective can lead to some pretty amazing blunders. Robert H. Goddard was a visionary trailblazer in the early days of rocket science. NASA lauded his accomplishments in a 2004 online article: "Now known as the father of modern rocketry, Goddard's significant achievements in rocket propulsion have contributed immensely to the scientific exploration of space."[1] The first to build a liquid-fuel rocket and launch a rocket payload, he is credited with 214 patents, and his list of rocketry firsts is astounding.

But despite his amazing scientific work, Goddard was the subject of some shameful treatment.

In 1920, the Smithsonian published his original paper, "A Method for Reaching Extreme Altitudes," in which he included a small section stressing that rockets could be used to send payloads to the Moon. Unfortunately, the press got wind of this and the next day, the *New York Times* wrote a scathing editorial denouncing his theories as folly. Goddard was ridiculed and made to look like a fool.[1]

The *New York Times* editorial mocked Goddard and questioned whether he knew any more than a high school student. It's hard to quantify the arrogance it took for newspaper reporters who knew little about rocketry to criticize the work of a man clearly out of their league. Unchecked control over their news forum, coupled with an overestimation of their own self-importance, emboldened their abuse of journalistic privilege.

This account is instructive. Today, the content of mainstream scientific journals passes through chokepoints controlled by evolutionists. They've used that control to criticize several biological organs as "poorly designed"—especially the human eye. Does scientific evidence justify these assertions, or does it point to a deliberately limited frame of reference that these critics have on biological systems they simply do not fully understand?

Playing "Gotcha" with God

Evolutionists believe they have discovered numerous design flaws in living organisms. According to them, flaws arise because organisms evolve bit by bit over long ages in a ruthless struggle to survive. Death, not intelligence, is embraced as the means that fractions out the DNA needed to build new traits in a process that somehow operates without thought or purpose. Brown University's Kenneth Miller explains how his evolutionary beliefs contrast with seeing creatures as being made by a wise, benevolent God:

> Though some insist that life as we know it sprang from a Grand Designer's Original blueprints, Biology offers new evidence that organisms were cobbled together layer upon layer by a timeless tinkerer called evolution.[2]

Anything cobbled together by a tinkerer would likely have many mistakes—especially when compared to the creations of a craftsman. Thus, the evolutionist's argument is that the presence of design flaws reveals evolutionary tinkering and not the work of God. Richard Dawkins thinks he sees some huge problems in how the human eye is put together. To him, creationists are caught in a dilemma: Either God did not design the eye or He made mistakes.

Dawkins begins with cells capable of detecting incoming

131

light. These have photosensitive elements at one end and a nerve at the other end that conveys signals to the brain (Figure 1).

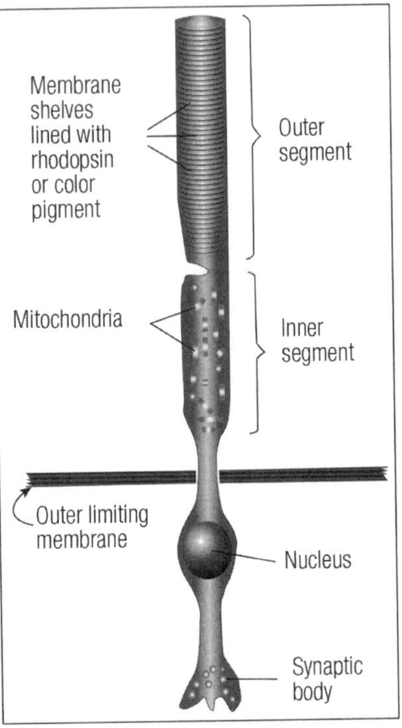

Light enters the front of the human eye, while the brain is located behind it. Other eyes are built in a manner called *verted*, where the photosensitive elements face the front and the nerves go out the back. But vertebrate eyes are built *inverted*, where the photosensitive elements face the back and the nerves face front. The nerves come together at a specific location and U-turn out the back.

Figure 1: *A rod photoreceptor cell. The outer segment is the light-sensitive portion. The inner segment and nucleus are essential for cell metabolism and replenish the outer segment. The synaptic body connects the photoreceptor to the nervous system that transfers data from the receptor to the brain.*

The "Poor Design" Mantra

Dawkins popularized the belief that anyone can simply look at the eye's inverted layout and plainly see that it is a foolish design, that it is "wired backwards."

Any engineer would naturally assume that the photocells would point towards the light, with their wires leading backwards towards the brain. He would laugh at any suggestion that the photocells might point away from the light, with their wires departing on the side *nearest* the light. Yet this is exactly what happens in all vertebrate retinas. Each photocell is, in effect, wired in backwards, with its wire sticking out on the side nearest the light. The wire has to travel over the surface of the retina, to a point where it dives through a hole in the retina (the so-called 'blind spot') to join the optic nerve. This means that the light, instead of being granted an unrestricted passage to the photocells, has to pass through a forest of connecting wires, presumably suffering at least some attenuation and distortion (actually probably not much, still, it is the *principle* of the thing that would offend any tidy-minded engineer!).[3]

Dawkins was not the lone evolutionary voice on the subject. Kenneth Miller later grabbed the baton, claiming, "Evolution, unlike design, works by the modification of pre-existing structures....[It] does not produce perfection." His prime example? "The eye, that supposed paragon of intelligent design, is a perfect place to start."[4] Miller parrots Dawkins' disapproval:

Given the basics of this wiring, how would you orient the retina with respect to the direction of light? Quite naturally, you (and any other designer) would choose the orientation that produces the highest degree of visual quality. No one, for example, would suggest that the neural wiring connections should be placed on the side that faces the light, rather than on the side away from it. Incredibly, this is *exactly* how the human retina is constructed.[4]

Like Dawkins, Miller admits there is no evidence of poor eye performance: "None of this should be taken to suggest that the eye functions poorly. Quite the contrary, it is a superb visual instrument that serves us exceedingly well." But the eye is not built the way *he* feels it should be: "The key to the argument from design is not whether or not an organ or system works well, but whether its basic structural plan is the obvious product of design. The structural plan of the eye is not."[4] Devotees of Miller should recognize that he subtlely changed the basis for his criticism from an objective standard to his subjective opinion.

However, many examples of complicated biological systems with multiple parts working together were published in scientific literature at the same time Dawkins was making his comments. In this sea of documented biological complexity, evolutionary claims of poor design—without documented poor performance—rang hollow.

So, Francis Ayala, an evolutionary biologist and American Academy for the Advancement of Science president, joined the party. He began asserting that visual problems are caused by poor design. First, he claimed:

We know that some deficiencies are not just imperfections, but are outright dysfunctional, jeopardizing the very function the organ or part is supposed to serve. In the human eye, the optic nerve forms inside the eye cavity and creates a blind spot as it crosses the retina.[5]

But then, in a broad-brushed flail against intelligent design, he pronounced that "it is not only that organisms and their parts are less than perfect, but also that deficiencies and dysfunctions are pervasive, evidencing 'incompetent' rather than 'intelligent' design."[6] However, the real experts—actual neuroscientists—weren't documenting dysfunctional eyes.

Bad Design or Optimized Design?

Dawkins and other evolutionists may think that since the performance of *one* particular eye trait isn't maximized then it's irrelevant to investigate the entity as a functional whole. This practice leaves them ignorant of good reasons for design tradeoffs or other involved factors.

There is no excuse for this "poor design" blunder. When Dawkins, Miller, and Ayala made their claims, abundant existing information related how retinal tissues marvelously balance design solutions to several competing physical challenges—simultaneously—to begin converting light fluctuations into useful information. Engineers regularly need to concurrently satisfy numerous competing interests. When engineers optimize a design, they find solutions for several conflicting demands—a hallmark of sophisticated engineering.[7]

In the eye, this light-processing optimization requires 1) a mechanism to detect light, 2) a quick replenishment of that light-detecting mechanism to enable its extended use in large quantities of light, which tends to destroy tissue, 3) the removal of heat from the highly metabolic process before the heat destroys protein function, 4) the removal of heat from light focused on the retina, and 5) the prevention of light reflecting inside the eye after it passes through the photoreceptors. For human eyes, how could engineers optimally balance these major factors so the retina can work properly? They'd solve the problem by building an inverted retina! Photoreceptors must be inverted and embedded in the retinal pigment epithelium, a cell layer just outside the retina.

This vital tissue removes waste and helps remove heat from the rapidly regenerating receptors.[8] Its black granule pigment prevents light-scattering. The choroid's extensive network of blood vessels supports the high metabolic needs of photoreceptors and functions like a car radiator to absorb additional heat.[9] Researchers have known for decades that the "uninsulated" nerve fibers leaving the photoreceptors spread apart, making this layer light-transparent.[10] In addition, retinal Müller cells conduct light from front to back like fiber optic cables. One paper described their remarkable properties: "The increasing refractive index together with their funnel shape at nearly constant light-guiding capability make them ingeniously designed light collectors."[11] This enables the light-sensitive molecules to detect light regardless of which way the retina is oriented.

Simply put, if our eyes were built according to evolutionists' expectations, we'd all be blind.

"Poor Design" Claims Are Spectacularly Wrong

One neurophysicist effectively summed up how human eyes couldn't be more sensitive to light:

> "If you imagine this, it is remarkable: a photon, the smallest physical entity with quantum properties of which light consists, is interacting with a biological system consisting of billions of cells, all in a warm and wet environment," says [Rockefeller University professor Alipasha] Vaziri. "The

136

response that the photon generates survives all the way to the level of our awareness despite the ubiquitous background noise. Any man-made detector would need to be cooled and isolated from noise to behave the same way."[12]

One research study simply concludes, "The retina is revealed as an optimal structure designed for improving the sharpness of images."[13] Another account extolls the eye's extraordinary performance: "Photoreceptors operate at the outermost boundary allowed by the laws of physics, which means they are as good as they can be, period."[14]

A 2014 report on the vast contradictory scientific evidence against long-standing claims of poor eye design stated:

Having the photoreceptors at the back of the retina is not a design constraint, it is a design feature. The idea that the vertebrate eye, like a traditional front-illuminated camera, might have been improved somehow if it had only been able to orient its wiring behind the photoreceptor layer, like a cephalopod, is folly.[15]

Every statement by Dawkins, Miller, Ayala, and others about the eye's poor design—from photocells being "wired backwards" to the eye being "outright dysfunctional"—is scientifically incorrect. "Folly" accurately describes their blunder. Their ignorance surpasses that of the journalists who criticized the aeronautical genius of Robert Goddard. By asserting that our eye's design isn't what a *sensible* human engineer would do, these evolutionists mock God. Now, their smug ridicule of eye anatomy and their claims that it is exhibit A for poor design are embarrassingly exposed as a clear scientific blunder.

Time and truth go hand in hand. Goddard was right and the journalists wrong. NASA noted:

A day after Apollo 11 set off for the Moon, in July of 1969, the New York Times printed a correction to its 1920 editorial section, stating that "it is now definitely established that a rocket can function in a vacuum as well as in an atmosphere. *The Times* regrets the error."[16]

Though greatly belated, the *Time's* humble retraction is honorable. Science shows that God is also due a retraction. Time will reveal how well humility fits into the "struggle for survival" mindset of the evolutionists who have denied His engineering genius and creative craftsmanship.

References

1. Marconi, E. M. Robert Goddard: A Man and His Rocket. Posted on NASA.gov March 9, 2004, accessed July 15, 2016.
2. Miller, K. R. 1994. Life's Grand Design. *Technology Review.* 97 (2): 24-32.
3. Dawkins, R. 1987. *The Blind Watchmaker.* New York: W. W. Norton & Co, 93.
4. Miller, Life's Grand Design.
5. Ayala, F. J. 2007. *Darwin's Gift to Science and Religion.* Washington, DC: Joseph Henry Press, 22.
6. Ibid, 155.
7. Guliuzza, R. 2012. *Clearly Seen: Constructing Solid Arguments for Design.* Dallas, TX: Institute for Creation Research, 32-33.
8. Anderson, D. H., S. K. Fisher, and R. H. Steinberg. 1978. Mammalian cones: Disc shedding, phagocytosis and renewal. *Investigative Ophthalmology and Visual Science.* 17 (2): 117-133.
9. Parver, L. M., C. R. Auker, and D. O. Carpenter. 1983. Choroidal blood flow: III. Reflexive control in human eyes. *Archives of Ophthalmology.* 101 (10): 1604-1606.
10. Hamilton, H. S. 1985. The Retina of the Eye—An Evolutionary Roadblock. *Creation Research Society Quarterly.* 22 (2): 59-64.
11. Franze, K. et al. 2007. Müller cells are living optical fibers in the vertebrate retina. *Proceedings of the National Academy of Science.* 104 (20): 8287-8292.
12. Study suggests humans can detect even the smallest units of light. Rockefeller University news release. Posted on newswire.rockefeller.edu July 20, 2016, accessed July 21, 2016.
13. Labin, A. M. and E. N. Ribak. 2010. Retinal glial cells enhance human vision acuity. *Physical Review Letters.* 104 (15): 158102.
14. Angier, N. Seeing the Natural World With a Physicist's Lens. *New York Times.* Posted on nytimes.com November 1, 2010, accessed July 26, 2012. For the extended quote, see Thomas, B.

Eye Optimization in Creation. *Creation Science Update*. Posted on ICR.org November 23, 2010.

15. Hewitt, J. Fiber optic light pipes in the retina do much more than simple image transfer. *Phys. org*. Posted on phys.org July 21, 2014, accessed July 21 2016.

16. Marconi, Robert Goddard: A Man and His Rocket.

14

Haeckel's Embryos Born of Evolutionary Imagination

Summary

Haeckel's embryos adds to the long list of frauds in evolutionary theory. In 1874, Ernst Haeckel published a set of drawings that allegedly depict the development stages of a human embryo. They show a fish-like form changing into a salamander-like form, then a turtle-like form, then a pig-like mammal, then finally a baby. Evolutionists conjure up imaginary visions of these embryos supposedly reenacting our evolutionary history as they develop. Eventually, in the words of famous evolutionist Stephen Gould, they were discovered to be "fraudulent." Haeckel so grossly distorted the embryos that they went beyond artistic license. According to another evolutionist, "It looks like it's turning out to be one of the most famous fakes in biology." Thankfully, mainstream science journals have recognized the illegitimacy of Haeckel's embryos. But the drawings are continually reprinted in standard biology textbooks. Why is that? It looks like the facts are somewhat secondary to evolutionary propaganda.

"Generations of biology students may have been misled by a famous set of drawings of embryos published 123 years ago by the German biologist Ernst Haeckel."[1] *Science* magazine is referring to Haeckel's sketches of diverse animal embryos first published in 1874 (Figure 1). They report that Haeckel fraudulently minimized major differences between animals at the earliest developmental stages. This fraud is peculiar because it is being "rediscovered" by new research. Remarkably, *Science* notes that some embryologists of Haeckel's day had doubts about the drawing's accuracy, and his peers actually got him to admit he used "artistic license." Yet these drawings (or similar reproduc-

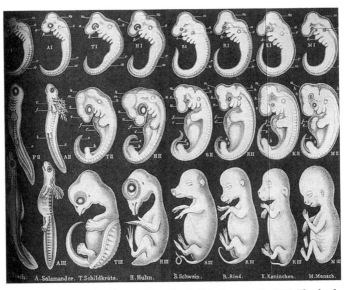

Figure 1: Illustration of embryos in Ernst Haeckel's Anthropogenie, 1874. *The sketches give a false impression that embryos of diverse vertebrates are nearly identical in a "primitive" fish-like form during early development. Many biology textbooks reproduce similar sketches. Research shows broad differences in embryonic shape and developmental pathways.*

tions) have been incorporated into nearly every major biology textbook ever since.[2] So, unlike Piltdown Man, *Archaeoraptor*, and other evolutionary frauds that only temporarily duped everyone, Haeckel's blunder misleads to this day.

Thus, *present* biology students are still deceived by a complicated tangle of misleading ideas that clever evolutionists regularly attach to Haeckel's fraudulent drawings.

Misleading Drawings and Concepts Promote Evolution

I didn't escape being misled. In 1975 my sophomore biology textbook referred to a drawing very similar to Haeckel's. Like most students absorbing this information for their first—and possibly only—time, I was surprised by the incredible fish-like similarity of all early embryos...especially humans. The visual evidence looked undeniable.

These drawings persuasively promoted three powerful evolutionary concepts. First, life evolved from "primitive" animals to complex humans. This "fact" is seen in the supposedly nonhuman structures that humans possess during development. My textbook commented, "For example, the early human embryo has a well-developed tail and also a series of gill pouches in the pharyngeal region."[3]

Second, as my textbook went on to say, "Human and fish embryos resemble each other because human beings and fish share a common remote ancestry."[3] It presented the remarkable similarity of the embryos in the illustration as strong evidence for a universal common ancestor.

Third, a synopsis of the evolutionary history of life on Earth

143

emerges as scientists map out all stages of embryonic development for every species. Remarkably, the stages of embryonic development for organisms, called *ontogeny*, supposedly reenacted or "recapitulated" their evolutionary history through time, which was called their *phylogeny*. Haeckel's embryos seemed to portray time-lapse pictures of evolution itself.

Those concepts remain cemented in contemporary evolutionary thinking. During medical school in 1992, my graduate-level human development textbook contained the same drawings and concepts.[4]

In 2001, Harvard's Ernst Mayr included Haeckel's exact embryos in his definitive work on evolution. Referencing them, he reaffirmed that only evolution explains why "the embryos of birds and mammals develop gill slits, like fish embryos."[5] Mayr detailed how he believed embryology demonstrated both universal common ancestry and recapitulation:

An early human embryo, for instance, is very similar not only to embryos of other mammals (dog, cow, mouse), but in its early stages even to those of reptiles, amphibians, and fishes...[the] study of the embryonic stages very often shows how a common ancestral stage gradually diverges in different branches of the ancestral tree...[that] in certain features, as in the gill pouches, the mammalian embryo does indeed recapitulate the ancestral condition...[which] this is the same reason why all terrestrial vertebrates (tetrapods) develop gill arches at a certain stage in their ontogeny.[5]

As a student, I implicitly accepted concepts built from Haeckel's drawings as truthful. Belief in evolution seemed reasonable. Unfortunately, I was deceived by the picture's and concept's extreme misrepresentation of reality.

Haeckel's Drawings Are a Spectacular Fraud

Though *Science*'s article labeled Haeckel a fraud, it's possible that *Science* could also report misleading beliefs. To be fair, Haeckel was using 19th-century equipment, and he did not hide every embryonic difference. Considering these mitigating factors, Robert Richards of the University of Chicago argues that *intentional* fraud by Haeckel has not been proven. He suggests that Haeckel critic Michael Richardson presents the embryonic research findings in ways that "exaggerates their differences from Haeckel's images." Richards also argues that Haeckel shouldn't be the sole scapegoat for perpetuating this misinformation. He points out how evolutionary embryologists since Haeckel have also advanced his views, so "actually, these recent embryologists ought to have been judged more culpable, given the increase of knowledge, standards, and instrumentation during the last 125 years."[6]

However, Michael Richardson makes the case that the magnitude of the true embryonic dissimilarities concealed by Haeckel indicates intentional fraud to promote evolution. He claims, "Unfortunately, Haeckel was overzealous. When we compared his drawings with real embryos, we found that he showed many details incorrectly. For example, we found variations in embryonic size, external form, and segment number which he did not show."[7] As he sums up, "It looks like it's turning out to be one of the most famous fakes in biology."[8]

Harvard's Stephen Jay Gould, a zealous evolutionist himself, frames the legacy of Haeckel's behavior:

> I do dislike the common phrase "artistic license," especially for its parochially smug connotation (when used by scientists) that creative humanists care little for empirical accuracy. (After all, the best artistic "distortions" record great skill and conscious intent.) But I don't know how else to describe the work of Haeckel. To cut to the quick of this drama: Haeckel had exaggerated the similarities by idealizations and omissions. He also, in some cases—in a procedure that can only be called fraudulent—simply copied the same figure over and over again…. Haeckel's drawings, despite their noted inaccuracies, entered into the most impenetrable and permanent of all quasi-scientific literatures: standard student textbooks of biology…. Once ensconced in textbooks, misinformation becomes cocooned and effectively permanent, because, as stated above, textbooks copy from previous texts.[9]

Exposing Haeckel-like textbook drawings as fraudulent is important, but the story of deception is far from over. The concepts attached to them are even more misleading.

Imaginary Gill Slits, Tails, and Biogenic Laws

Looking at the embryos in Figure 2, much of evolutionary embryology stands on the belief that folds in the neck region are truly gill slits and, for the human, that the long stretch of vertebral tissue is honestly a tail. Darwin appealed to that belief when he asserted that embryos recapitulate the *adult* stages of their ancestors in evolutionary history. He says, "It is highly probable that with many animals the embryonic or larval stages show us, more or less completely, the condition of the progenitor of the whole group in its adult state."[10] How can Darwin or other evolutionists see things like evolutionary progenitors or gill slits? Only by imagination.

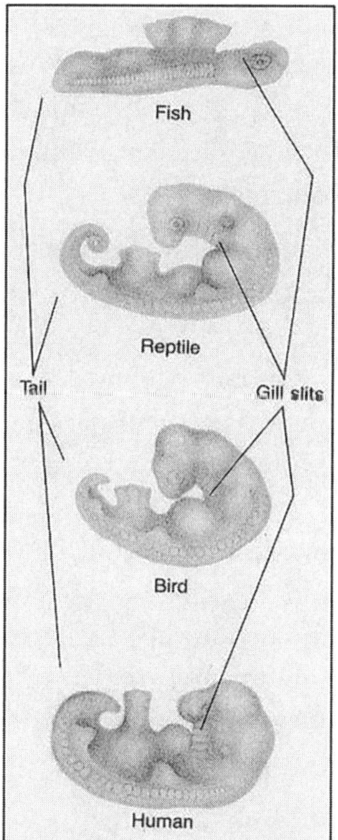

Darwin's invocation of imagination into evolutionary scenarios legitimatized plugging colossal data gaps with evolution's look-imagine-see methodology. Darwin visualized a bear evolving into a whale, a light-sensitive spot evolving into an eye, and embryos as reenacting their adult evolutionary progenitors. He *looked* at a feature of nature, *imagined* an evolutionary origin, and then *saw* what he expected.

The history of evolutionism shows how advocates can simply look at bones from Piltdown England and see ape features in a human skull, or look at bones embedded in the soft tissue of a whale's underbelly and see "whale hips," or see "primitive" features in a living fish, or how Richard Dawkins can look at a human

Figure 14-7 The evolutionary origin of certain structures can be inferred by comparing the embryological development of related organisms.

Figure 2: Biology textbook embryo illustration example. The "gill slits" on the reptile, bird, and human as well as the "tail" on human are fictitious. The folds of skin in the neck area never develop into gills and no evolutionary relationship can be inferred from them.

147

retina and plainly see that it's "wired backwards."[11] All of these instances have turned out to be blunders because evolutionists simply project evolutionary ideas onto any given finding, and, via their fertile imaginations, clearly see just what they were looking for.

Shouldn't students be skeptical when they're told that evolutionists can simply look at folds in embryos and see gill slits? The truth is that these are only folds of tissue in the pharynx region of vertebrates during the pharyngula stage of development. For mammals, birds, and reptiles, they *never* develop into a structure that is in any way like fish gills. In humans, for instance, this fold tissue develops into cartilage or bone for the jaw, inner ear, hyoid, and voice box. Muscles for the face, temple, and neck form out of them, as well as the thyroid, parathyroid, and thymus glands. No evidence exists that they ever resembled an adult fish or that throughout human history they lost the ability to form fish-like structures and now form new ones.

Regarding Haeckel's biogenic law of recapitulation, Richardson's work in the 1990s demonstrated that concept was utterly incorrect.[12] His results confirmed what Keith Thompson, president of the Academy of Natural Sciences, declared in 1988: "Surely the biogenic law is as dead as a doornail."[13]

The human "tail" is another misnomer born of evolutionism's look-imagine-see methodology. What we actually see through time are early precursors to the spine forming the axial skeleton (skull to coccyx). In a slightly lagging sequence, the rest of the embryo grows from head-to-rump on this foundational framework. So, when evolutionists see a lower portion of the axial skeleton where the embryo is yet to grow, they see a transient "tail." In their imaginations, human embryos are recapitu-lating their reptilian past. But there is *never* a tail. The embryo grows down to its coccyx, which begins anchoring developing muscles of the pelvic floor.

How much of the evolutionary story makes sense if human embryos never have gill slits or a tail?

What a Tangled Web We Weave

Embarrassed that his exposure of Haeckel's fraud had become a "Creationist cause celebre," Richardson later insisted that "data from embryology are fully consistent with Darwin-ian evolution."[14] Like Haeckel, Richardson began misleading people by declaring that an organism's "shared developmental program" that showed "that development in different animals is controlled by common genetic mechanisms" fit evolutionary theory. The fact is evolutionists never expected common genetic mechanisms. They were "shocked" and "stunned" upon discov-ery, and only pivoted to embrace relabeled "conserved" mecha-nisms *after* detection. It was creationists who had first discussed common designs for common features.[15]

Students should be aware of evolutionary authority—such as when Jerry Coyne altered his approach to salvage recapitu-lation. He claims, "Embryonic stages don't look like the adult forms of their ancestors, as Haeckel claimed, but like the *embry-onic* forms of ancestors."[16] How? Evolution doesn't erase devel-opmental plans; it somehow keeps adding new information. According to Coyne, "It's usually easier to simply tack less dra-matic changes onto what is already a robust and basic develop-mental plan….This 'adding new stuff onto old' principle also explains why the sequence of developmental changes mirrors the sequence of organisms."[16]

But Coyne misleads. The "adding new stuff onto old" principle is born of evolution's look-imagine-see mechanism. Coyne's scheme has many inconsistencies. He admits the sequence "is neither strict nor inevitable: not every feature of an ancestor's embryo appears in its descendants, nor do all stages of development unfold in strict evolutionary order." He adds that plants "have dispensed with nearly all traces of their ancestry during development."[16] Yet two decades prior, Keith Thomson foresaw Coyne's "add on" principle as absurd since the development of a species "would be almost infinitely long, as the sequence of characteristics of every ancestor, every evolutionary divergence, was rerun…through the adding on of new stages—terminal additions—to the developmental history of the immediate ancestor."[17]

Lessons Learned

Watching a single cell assimilate resources and self-develop into an extraordinary creature should evoke a sense of awe for our Creator in any mind not blinded by naturalistic thinking. Ironically, unbridled imagination actually blinds some minds. As biochemist Michael Behe noted regarding Haeckel's embryos, "The story of the embryos is an object lesson in seeing what you want to see."[18]

References
1. Pennisi, E. 1997. Haeckel's Embryos: Fraud Rediscovered. *Science.* 277 (5331): 1435.
2. Luskin, C. What Do Modern Textbooks Really Say About Haeckel's Embryos? *Discovery Institute.* Posted on discovery.org March 27, 2007, accessed August 29, 2016.
3. Keeton, W. T. 1972. *Biological Science,* 2nd ed. New York: W. W. Norton & Company, 550.

4. Moore, K. L. 1989. *Before We Are Born,* 3rd ed. Philadelphia, PA: W. B. Saunders Company, 70.
5. Mayr, E. 2001. *What Evolution Is.* New York: Basic Books, 27-30.
6. Richards, R. J. 2009. Haeckel's embryos: fraud not proven. *Biology and Philosophy.* 24: 147-154.
7. Richardson, M. K. et al. 1998. Haeckel, Embryos, and Evolution. *Science.* 280 (5366): 983.
8. Pennisi, Haeckel's Embryos.
9. Gould, S. J. 2000. Abscheulich! (Atrocious!) Haeckel's distortions did not help Darwin. *Natural History.* 109 (2): 42-49.
10. Darwin, C. 1859. *On the Origin of Species by Means of Natural Selection.* London: John Murray, 395.
11. Dawkins, R. 1987. *The Blind Watchmaker.* New York: W. W. Norton & Co., 93.
12. Richardson, M. K. et al. 1997. There is no highly conserved embryonic stage in the vertebrates: implications for current theories of evolution and development. Anatomy and Embryology. 196 (2): 91-106. Also, Thomas, B. 2012. Do People Have 'Gill Slits' in the Womb? *Creation Science Update.* Posted on ICR.org July 20, 2012, accessed September 1, 2016.
13. Thomson, K. S. 1988. Marginalia: Ontogeny and phylogeny recapitulated. *American Scientist.* 76 (3): 273-275.
14. Richardson, Haeckel, Embryos, and Evolution.
15. Guliuzza, R. 2015. Major Evolutionary Blunders: Evolutionary Predictions Fail the Reality Test. *Acts & Facts.* 44 (9): 17-19.
16. Coyne, J. 2009. *Why Evolution Is True.* New York: Viking, 78. Emphasis in original.
17. Thomson, Marginalia, 273-274.
18. Behe, M. J. Teach Evolution—And Ask Hard Questions. *New York Times.* Posted on nytimes. com August 13, 1999, accessed September 28, 2016.

15

Imagining That Life Is Only Chemistry

Summary

Since many evolutionists believe that matter and natural law are all that exists, then they declare "Life is only chemistry!" That has been the rallying cry, and method, of evolutionary theory for over 150 years. And yet, their explanations for how life originated remain woefully inadequate. The biggest difficulty is that it is becoming increasingly clear that life is *not* chemistry— life is based on *information*. Evolutionists Sara Walker and Paul Davies observed that "although it has been notoriously difficult to pin down precisely what is it that makes life so distinctive and remarkable, there is general agreement that its informational aspect is one key property, perhaps *the* key property." Explaining the information of life is often pointed to as the biggest problem in biology. As chemist George Whitesides says, "How remarkable is life? The answer is: very. Those of us who deal in networks of chemical reactions know of nothing like it." Evolution fails at explaining the spontaneous appearance of information, and thus life, in a material universe. But it makes perfect sense to those who believe the universe was created by an all-powerful Mind.

Some people who watch American football only see players running in zigzags and senselessly colliding until there is a pile of men lying on the field. But to the cheering fans, they just witnessed a quarterback read the defense and call out adjustments to a complicated strategy, followed by precise player movements purposively choreographed like a ballet. This group knows the big picture of the game, which includes the mini-battles between individual players. That insight fits other areas as well.

Evolutionists and creationists seem to debate endlessly about everything. Complicated technical arguments about amino acids, nucleotides, meteorites, thermodynamics, and biological mechanisms may come across as disconnected and irrelevant to daily life, but these seemingly trivial debates are like two opposing football players' mini-battle. Understanding how everything fits together is easier if a person can see the bigger picture.

Therefore, stepping back from amino acid debates reveals that their context is a widespread provocative claim that "life is only chemistry." For instance, two evolutionary authorities recently said, "Indeed, as van Helmont concluded in 1648, and as is even today the rallying cry at conferences on the origin and evolution of life, it seems quite clear that 'all life is chemistry.'"[1] Whether that is true or not may affect daily life in areas as diverse as health care policies, religion, or the wisdom of tax expenditures on projects searching for aliens.

Evidence shows that evolutionary assertions that life is only chemistry constitute another major blunder. While significant, that lesson is secondary. More important is how a "life is chemistry" declaration illustrates that quarrels over details are truly significant when they are nested in opposing worldviews. Discovering the concealed links between basic research and worldviews is fascinating.

Did God Create Nature, or Did Nature Create Itself?

Detail-level origins disputes ultimately progress to answer this big-picture question: Did God create nature, or did nature create itself? God, in this sense, would reflect His attribute as a sufficient cause so that nature could be an effect. Ideally, studying the properties of nature should indicate one way or another whether God was a necessary cause or whether nature by itself is sufficient (meaning God isn't necessary). Realistically, however, researchers begin work by structuring their research efforts presupposing that one explanation is true. Knowing a worldview's assumptions is the first step to understanding how details like chemical bonds and molecular shapes get interpreted.

The condensed version of those who start with a "God creates nature" position is that they generally hold that matter and natural law proceed from, and are shaped by, God's pre-existing mind. God, His thoughts, and information—all immaterial—come first and matter later. God's mind, not matter, is the ultimate reality.

The exact opposite presupposition guides research for those embracing the "nature creates itself" view. They hold that the physical universe is the entirety of reality. A key assumption is that matter and some properties of nature are self-existent. They approach research presupposing that the way natural laws govern the interactions of matter will give rise to everything else.

Focusing on the "nature creates itself" view, also known as *materialism*, illustrates how adherents of a worldview risk establishing it as scientific dogma. This happens when they automatically use it to shape research plans.

How Worldviews and Research Programs Shape Each Other

The first step in starting a theory about life's origin is to define what life is. Everyone knows that living things grow, reproduce, adapt, and metabolize. However, these functions only describe what living things *do*, but not what life *is*. A recent scientific article's headline, "Why Life Is Physics, Not Chemistry,"[2] exemplifies that the basic premise of materialistic models will be some type of natural process. Definitions must align with the worldview, even if they are counterintuitive. Within materialism, declarations such as "life is chemistry" or "life is physics" define what life is.

Still, for many people it is somewhat odd to declare that life is either physics or chemistry. Something is different in a living person and missing from an essentially dead person maintained on life support—even though, theoretically, all tissues (except the brain) may be transplanted from that person's body to the living person. What exactly is maintained by the living person's biochemical processes? If those processes could be fixed in the body on life support, would life return? Does physics explain why living things seem to act with willful, goal-directed behaviors? Living creatures don't want just any resource but *strive* for the best ones. They *want* to reproduce. They *want* to live. People know they may order a pound of meat but not a pound of life. Nor can they acquire a similar quantity of consciousness or information or volition. Given these distinctions that physics and chemistry have yet to explain, we could simply declare the current scientific status—which is that so far neither human senses nor instrumentation has weighed or otherwise measured *life*.

There is a reason materialists extrapolate past the supporting evidence. Believing that nature created itself, they are constrained to exclude non-materialistic explanations. By definition, something that is beyond the realm of human detection is mystical, not material—which describes our current understanding of life. One future possibility is that life itself may be materially quantified and possibly duplicated. But a second possibility is that it may remain mystical. In fact, it may be immaterial. However, many scientists will structure research programs where the criteria to rule out the first possibility are exceedingly high. For example, this means that no matter how many chemical experiments result only in chemistry and not in life, something like the "life is chemistry" premise survives—since only materialistic explanations are conceivable. This finally takes us to understanding how different worldviews shape research programs.

Most people are uninformed and little concerned with research programs. However, in a scientific age, research programs are indispensable to achieving a dominant worldview. Why? First, a program and its underlying worldview vigorously feed each other. Second, research programs, with their attendant presuppositions, *control* what questions are considered legitimate, what research paths are acceptable, what research projects are allowable (i.e., funded), what views should be opposed, and what interpretations of results are permitted.[3] If the same "rallying cry" inspires similar programs across research institutions, conformity may be enforced and denial of publication may muzzle contrary voices.

This explains how materialism's declaration—not a conclusion—that life is physics or chemistry initiates and guides research programs. Its scientists already believe that complex molecules arise from simple chemical elements and that simple life will emerge from complex molecules. Supposedly, starting with only matter and law, a conscious mind—one capable of deciphering this whole preceding scenario—could arise through countless struggles for survival. Then, perhaps, some of those conscious minds while still in their primitive state will create the notion of God.

Research programs monopolize what findings are reported as science. Thus, we now understand why disputes over methodologies, details, and bias flowing from these programs will be the realm of debate between creationists and evolutionists. It also illustrates how a debate about whether life is chemistry is actually a debate about worldviews.

Materialists Declare "Life Is Chemistry"

Widespread belief that cellular function was extremely simple may explain why early researchers pursued chemistry-based scenarios.[4] Unfortunately, invoking imagination into scientific scenarios is conveniently overlooked in historical accounts.

Darwin imagined a scenario in which just the right environmental conditions craft life. Evolutionist John Priscu notes:

It was Charles Darwin who first posed an explanation for life's origin that complemented his evolutionary theory of life on Earth. In a letter written in 1871 to botanist Joseph Hooker, Darwin envisioned: "It is often said that all the conditions for the first production of a living organism are present, which could ever have been present. But if (and Oh! what a big if!) we could conceive in some warm little pond, with all sorts of ammonia and phosphoric salts, light, heat, electricity, etc., present, that a protein compound was chemically formed ready to undergo still more complex changes, at the present day such matter would be instantly devoured or absorbed, which would not have been the case before living creatures were formed."[5]

Darwin may merit a pass on thinking that life is simple due to the limited information of his time. But his introduction of the look-imagine-see methodology into science is contrary to science's distinguishing observation-based methods of learning about nature.

Today, complicated chemical reactions are manufactured everywhere, yet their results have no resemblance to living things. And yet, researchers still invoke the look-imagine-see method and declare that life is chemistry? The materialistic assumption that nature creates itself remains. That mindset leads to imagination-based research programs conceived in minds that visualize—and tolerate—fantastic leaps of evolutionary progress that are achieved through self-coordinated chemical processes. Chemistry, or the hardware of life, remains the focus of research, as one report recently confirmed: "Instead, hardware has dominated the discussion, in accordance with the generally reductionist flavour of biology in recent decades, with its associated assumption that, ultimately, all life is nothing but chemistry."[6]

Life Is Not Chemistry: Correcting a Blunder that Harms Biology

Life-origins researchers Sara Walker and Paul Davies observed that "although it has been notoriously difficult to pin down precisely what is it that makes life so distinctive and remarkable, there is general agreement that its informational aspect is one key property, perhaps the key property."[7] Their paper explains in depth how information—not chemistry—is the key property of living things.

In a candid interview on their work, Walker stated, "Chemical-based approaches...have stalled at a very early stage of chemical complexity—very far from anything we would consider 'alive.' More seriously they suffer from conceptual shortcomings in that they fail to distinguish between chemistry and biology." To which Davies added, "To a physicist or chemist, life seems like 'magic matter'...[that] behaves in extraordinary ways that are unmatched in any other complex physical or chemical system." Unlike being *just* chemistry, living things actually "harness chemical reactions to enact a pre-programmed agenda, rather than being a slave to those reactions."[8]

A report on the work of physicist Nigel Goldenfeld and microbiologist Carl Woese bluntly synopsized their criticism of all-life-is-chemistry beliefs: "Goldenfeld and Woese say that biologists' closed way of thinking on this topic is embodied by the phrase: all life is chemistry. Nothing could be further from the truth, they say."[9] That author summarized the bold assessment of Goldenfeld and Woese's own paper that challenged the "rallying cry" that all life is chemistry, which, they concluded, "has arguably retarded the development of biology as a science, with disastrous consequences for its applications to medicine, ecology and the global environment."[10]

The Folly of Imagination-Based Research Programs

Reality differs radically from such self-affirming statements as "Darwin's 'warm little pond' idea was supported experimentally by two University of Chicago researchers [Miller and Urey] in the early 1950s."[11] Walker and Davies opened their paper by acknowledging, "Of the many open questions surrounding how life emerges from non-life, perhaps the most challenging is the vast gulf between complex chemistry and the simplest biology."[12] They quoted chemist George Whitesides, who stated, "How remarkable is life? The answer is: very. Those of us who deal in networks of chemical reactions know of nothing like it."[13] They reproved simplistic research programs like Miller and Urey's, saying, "Often the issue of defining life is sidestepped by assuming that if one can build a simple chemical system capable of Darwinian evolution, then the rest will follow suit and the problem of life's origin will de facto be solved."[14]

For those who believe that God created nature, there is also a note of caution. The Bible says that the Lord formed Adam from dust and then breathed into him the breath of life (Genesis 2:7). Did the breath of life turn simple chemistry into complex chemistry or impart something altogether different? Criticisms of life-is-chemistry programs must *not* be aimed solely at the simplicity of their stories and their trivial results—which may leave the impression that life could still somehow be complicated chemistry. The main problem remains evolution's invocation of wholesale imagination to build research programs that, paradoxically, are closed to considering all non-material explanations. Yet, life could be something totally distinct from chemistry, as even Walker and Davies acknowledged: "The heart of the issue is that we do not know whether the living state is 'just' very complex chemistry, or whether there is something fundamentally distinct about living matter."[15]

References

1. Goldenfeld, N. and C. Woese. 2011. Life Is Physics: Evolution as a Collective Phenomenon Far from Equilibrium. *Annual Review of Condensed Matter Physics.* 2: 375-399.

2. Why Life Is Physics, Not Chemistry. *MIT Technology Review.* Posted on technologyreview.com November 22, 2010, accessed September 27, 2016.

3. Gould, S. J. 2002. *The Structure of Evolutionary Theory.* Cambridge, MA: Harvard University Press, 61, 157-159, 451.

4. Meyer, S. C. 2009. *Signature in the Cell: DNA and the Evidence for Intelligent Design.* New York: HarperCollins, 43-44.

5. Priscu, J. C. Origin and Evolution of Life on a Frozen Earth. *National Science Foundation.* Posted on nsf.gov, accessed September 27, 2016.

6. Walker, S. I. and P. C. W. Davies. 2013. The algorithmic origins of life. *Journal of the Royal Society Interface.* 10 (79): 1-9.

7. Ibid, 1.

8. Derra, S. ASU researchers propose new way to look at the dawn of life. Arizona State University news release. Posted on asuncws.asu.edu December 12, 2012, accessed September 26, 2016.

9. Why Life Is Physics, Not Chemistry.

10. Goldenfeld and Woese, Life Is Physics, 375.

11. Priscu, Origin and Evolution of Life on a Frozen Earth.

12. Walker and Davies, The algorithmic origins of life, 1.

13. Ibid.

14. Ibid.

15. Ibid.

16

Neanderthals Were Subhuman in Imagination Only

Summary

A common evolutionary motif is the caveman-like Neanderthal. Big, hulking, and unintelligent, it has even become a cultural icon in movies and commercials. It started with Darwin. Neanderthal bones were just being discovered as he was publishing his influential book, and scientists following his lead quickly incorporated them into his theory. Neanderthals became the poster child for human evolution from ape-like animals. However, as more research surfaced, it became increasingly clear that this stereotype is dreadfully wrong. Genetic studies show that Neanderthals were at least 99.7% similar to modern humans. They made jewelry, built houses and handtools, learned basic chemistry, and even demonstrated spiritual sensitivity in religious burial rituals. As one evolutionist put it, "Next time you call someone a Neanderthal, better look in a mirror."

"So easy, a caveman could do it" is the witty slogan of a company hoping to lure customers to switch car insurance. The humorous catch to the commercial was the brutish-looking, yet endearing, Neanderthals living among us who found the slogan stereotyping them as dimwits were "not cool" or "hurtful." The fact that viewers could readily spot the standard view of Neanderthals shows how pervasive it is and how it dominates the popular perception.

Evolutionary beliefs—not known facts about Neanderthals—forced this misleading subhumanized caricature of them. Evolutionary imagination conjured up the ape-like, hairy, club-wielding, mentally underdeveloped savage because it fit their expectations of a missing link between an ape-like ancestor and humans, as seen in Figure 1. Rather than liberating scientific research, for decades this major evolutionary blunder sidetracked an accurate understanding of Neanderthals.

Imagining More Than Flesh on Neanderthal Bones

Charles Darwin hurt the scientific method when he injected the look-imagine-see methodology into the process of explaining the diversity of life on Earth.[1] This method of interpreting findings has led to one evolutionary blunder after another in which evolutionists develop a clear mental picture of just exactly what they are looking for…even though it does not exist. The mental projections of ape-like features onto Neanderthal bones is akin to the envisioned ape-like features of the human skull cap of Piltdown man.[2]

Neanderthals were named after the limestone cave of the Neander Valley near Dusseldorf, Germany, where their first

Figure 1: The popular view of Neanderthal man as an ape-like, hairy, club-wielding, mentally underdeveloped savage reigned for over 125 years. French paleontologist Marcellin Boule commissioned an early depiction of Neanderthal Man published in The Illustrated London News *in 1909 that became the basis for a misleading stereotype. Boule studied a skull discovered in 1908 at La Chapelle-aux-Saints in southwestern France and employed the look-imagine-see methodology to envision this drawing, which has been shown not to be the "accurate reconstruction of the prehistoric cave-man" the* London News *caption claimed.*

bones were discovered in 1856. Evolutionary ideas biased the interpretation of these bones just as these same ideas have prejudiced the understanding of different people groups found worldwide. Over 100 years later, the bestselling Life Nature Library series explained to lay audiences Neanderthals' place in human evolution:

> Darwin heard about these remarkable bones, yet never investigated them, but Huxley undertook a thorough study of the unprecedented skull. In the condition in which it was discovered, the cranium could hold 63 cubic inches of water; com-

plete, it would have contained 75 cubic inches, or as much as the skulls of living primitive tribesmen.[3]

In the evolutionary spectrum of ape to modern human as reflected in brain size, "primitive tribesmen" were expected to fall somewhere in between.

Readers of this series in eight languages and in 90 countries were treated to more imagination than just the brain size of "primitive" tribesmen. Sir Julian Huxley was also able to clearly visualize ape-like features in the skull of this supposed transition from ape to human:

> "Under whatever aspect we view this cranium," wrote Huxley in 1863, in his book *Zoological Evidence as to Man's Place in Nature*, "whether we regard its vertical depression, the enormous thickness of the supraciliary ridges, its sloping occiput, or its long and straight squamosal suture, we meet with apelike characteristics, stamping it as the most pithecoid [ape-like] of human crania yet discovered." Neanderthal man, Huxley concluded, was more nearly allied to the higher apes than the latter are to the lower apes, but for all of that he was a man.[3]

Scientific literature put Neanderthals into the evolutionary scheme as a type of transitional creature,[4] and pop culture reflected it. Movies that might seem like a spoof or a comedy, like the one advertised in Figure 2, shaped the public perception of Neanderthals and other "cavemen."[5]

Evolutionary Depictions of Neanderthals Were Stunningly Wrong

In the last decade, an astounding flood of documentation

poured in showing how Neanderthals are far more human than evolutionary stories depicted.[6] Views about diminished mental capacity were especially overturned. Infant brain development for Neanderthals was believed to follow "an ancestral mode of brain development, similar to that of our closest living relatives, the chimpanzees. In contrast, it was suggested that modern humans follow a uniquely derived mode of brain development just after birth," but "the new data indicate that Neanderthals followed largely similar modes of endocranial

Figure 2: The 1953 movie The Neanderthal Man reflected the evolutionary notion that Neanderthals were transitional creatures between apes and humans.

development to modern humans. These findings challenge the notion that human brain and cognitive development after birth is uniquely derived."[7]

The full sequencing of Neanderthal DNA showed it was at least 99.7% like that of living humans.[8] Neanderthals and other humans mated[9] and exchanged DNA that "in some places, such as the DNA related to the skin, the genetic instructions are as much as 70 percent Neanderthal and in other places there's virtually nothing from the species that's often portrayed as brutish cavemen." Therefore, the "next time you call someone a Neanderthal, better look in a mirror."[10]

Usually creatures, especially humans, mate only with others that they recognize as the same species. As a science reporter states, the fact of Neanderthals mating with people like us reveals that

"for a long time, the field of human evolution has imagined a fictional world where distinct human groups separated from one another and then remained distinct for long periods of time," Siepel [a Cold Spring Harbor Laboratory geneticist said]...."And we're just finding out on multiple time scales that's just not true."[11]

The evidence of Neanderthals as evolutionary transitions is being shown to be merely a mental construct that took on a life of its own following its wholesale adoption.

Possibly, the most remarkable findings are Neanderthal artifacts that reveal behaviors like those of all people throughout history. A simple search for published reports returns headlines like "Surprise: Neanderthals Were Fine Housekeepers," "Ancient Engraving Strengthens Case for Sophisticated Neandertals," "Ice age fashion showdown: Neanderthal capes versus human hoodies," "The Real Question: Who Didn't Have Sex with Neanderthals?," "Neandertals may have used chemistry to start fires," "Handaxe design reveals distinct Neanderthal cultures," "Neandertals made their own jewelry, new method confirms," "Maybe Neanderthals Weren't Such...Neanderthals," "Neanderthals Built Mysterious Stone Circles," and "Modern humans no brainier than Neanderthals, study finds."

The magnitude of the evolutionary blunder that Neanderthals were transitions between ape and human is accentuated in today's reconstructions of Neanderthals—which look like us.

The National Geographic Society commissioned a reconstruction of a Neanderthal woman based on the most current information from genetics, fossil evidence, and archaeology, as shown in Figure 3. The magazine reported, "'For the first time, anthropologists can go beyond fossils and peer into the actual genes of an extinct species of human,' said National Geographic's senior science editor, Jamie Shreeve, who oversaw the project." It also reports "that at least some Neanderthals would have had red hair, pale skin, and possibly freckles."[12]

Given the recent nature of this blunder over Neanderthals, how likely is it that evolutionists would risk another mistaken depiction of a "caveman" sporting imagined features? It is clear that evidence for evolution obtained from fragmentary fossil remains must still be derived from Darwin's look-imagine-see methodology. Another blunder concocted from fertile imaginations seems likely.

Another Imaginary "Authentic Look" at Early Human Life

Duke professor Adrian Bejan astutely observed that "in biology, evolution is largely a mental construct built on imagination, because the time scale of animal evolution is immense relative to the time available."[13] This clarifies why holes in evolutionary

Figure 3: The National Geographic Society commissioned a reconstruction of a Neanderthal woman named "Wilma" based on the latest information from genetics, fossil evidence, and archaeology. Artistic license constrained by evolutionary imagination still attempts to depict Wilma as a somewhat disheveled subhuman despite her underlying human features.

theory get filled with "evidence" that is later shown to be pure fantasy. Neanderthals appear to be one variety of humans bearing traits that people today still express. But evolutionary theory for human origins still requires primitive transitional forms between apes and humans.

In 2009 the Public Broadcasting Service grabbed the human evolution baton and used its popular show *NOVA* to produce a three-part special on human origins, called *Becoming Human*. *NOVA* retained the talented Graham Townsley as producer and Harvard paleoanthropologist Dan Leiberman as the technical consultant for human origins. They selected *Homo heidelbergensis* and *Homo erectus* to be depicted as subhuman links to an ape-like ancestor. Though fossil remains for both creatures are scarce, the program asserts that *Homo heidelbergensis* is the direct ancestor of Neanderthals.

Just as French paleontologist Marcellin Boule invoked wholesale imagination in 1909 to depict Neanderthals as cavemen, *NOVA* and Townsley did the same with *Homo heidelbergensis*. Filling the subhuman void left by Neanderthals, a *NOVA* actor was made to look like a primitive caveman complete with a "pronathic lower jaw" and "protruding" lips.[14] As costumed, he could star in either *Becoming Human* or the 1953 movie *The Neanderthal Man*. Fossils do not generally inform us of details about skin, hair, clothing, or behavior. Thus Leiberman, like Boule, invokes pure imagination to advise on these features. *NOVA*'s documentary of the series' production makes plain the imaginative element. "The skeleton of *Homo erectus* is different from a modern human," it said, "so Townsley's actors had to learn how to walk and run like an ancient hominin." And

Townsley describes how "Dan Lieberman, who is a well-known Harvard paleoanthropologist, is telling us all how he thinks we should go about imagining this hunting scene with *Homo erectus*."[15]

Becoming Human also conveyed scenes of an "evolving human society." Filling in where *Homo erectus* bones leave off, Dan Lieberman drew again on his imagination to instruct actors in blue suits on how to squat like apes and pick nits from each other's hair. The blue suits allowed for computer graphics artists to cover their bodies with hair and other primitive features. Townsley desired his lay audience to have a high level of confidence in *Becoming Human*'s imaginary scenarios, and he "says that working with computer graphics like this was new ground for him, but he hopes they will give viewers an authentic look at what early humans were like," and also that "the recreations" in his documentary will have "a new type of authenticity to them."[16]

Time and truth go hand in hand. Decades from now, *Becoming Human* may have as much credibility as *The Neanderthal Man* movie or be lumped in with other major evolutionary blunders. Its misleading information about Neanderthals was not something that just happened or can be blamed on pop culture. It started with evolutionary scientists and the scenarios they envision using Darwin's look-imagine-see methodology to fill in the missing data for their theory.

References

1. Guliuzza, R. 2016. Major Evolutionary Blunders: Haeckel's Embryos Born of Evolutionary Imagination. *Acts & Facts.* 45 (11): 16-18.
2. Guliuzza, R. 2015. Major Evolutionary Blunders: The Imaginary Piltdown Man. *Acts & Facts.* 44 (12): 12-14.

3. Moore, R. 1962. *Life Nature Library: Evolution*. New York: Time Incorporated, 130.
4. Trinkaus, E. and R. H. Tuttle. Neanderthal. *Encyclopaedia Britannica*. Posted on britannica.com January 29, 2015, accessed October 27, 2016.
5. Hadingham, E. Early Humans in Pop Culture. *NOVA*. Posted on pbs.org October 26, 2009, accessed October 27, 2016.
6. For a comprehensive catalog of Neanderthal behaviors like those of humans living today see Neanderthal Concept Has Imploded. *Creation Evolution Headlines*. Posted on crev.info February 22, 2016; Neanderthals Underestimated Again. *Creation Evolution Headlines*. Posted on crev.info May 27, 2016; and O'Leary, D. A Deep and Abiding Need for Neanderthals to Be Stupid. Why? *Evolution News and Views*. Posted on evolutionnews.org July 21, 2014.
7. Ponce de León, M. S. et al. 2016. Brain development is similar in Neanderthals and modern humans. *Current Biology*. 26 (14): R665-R666.
8. Complete Neanderthal Genome Sequenced. *National Institutes of Health News*. Posted on genome.gov May 5, 2010, accessed October 27, 2016.
9. Kuhlwilm, M. et al. 2016. Ancient gene flow from early modern humans into Eastern Neanderthals. *Nature*. 530 (7591): 429-433.
10. How much Neanderthal DNA do you have? Lots. *Associated Press*. Posted on foxnews.com January 29, 2014, accessed October 28, 2016.
11. Resnick, B. Humans and Neanderthals had sex. But was it for love? Posted on vox.com September 14, 2016, accessed September 27, 2016.
12. Braun, D. Photo in the News: DNA-Based Neanderthal Face Unveiled. Posted on news.nationalgeographic.com September 17, 2008, accessed November 7, 2016.
13. Bejan, A., J. D. Charles, and S. Lorente. 2014. The evolution of airplanes. *Journal of Applied Physics*. 116 (044901): 1-6.
14. Levin, D. Depicting Our Ancestors. *NOVA*. Posted on pbs.org. October 26, 2009, accessed October 27, 2016.
15. Ibid.
16. Ibid.

172

17

Evolutionary Psychology for Serious Tabloid Readers

Summary

Evolutionary psychology, formerly known as sociobiology, attempts to explain human behavior by referencing our evolutionary past. Men are attracted to curvaceous females because of better offspring, people bully because of its survival benefits, females cheat on their mates because of an evolutionary advantage, etc. Evolutionary psychology projects animal behavior onto humans. Much of the problem with evolutionary psychology is that it justifies certain behaviors as pre-determined that most societies consider to be morally wrong. Some evolutionists got in big trouble with other scientists, and others, when they justified rape as simply a male desire for sexual stimulation. Rape is a product of past selection pressure due to the reproductive success of rapist males. Evolutionist Joan Roughgarden called this explanation "the latest 'evolution made me do it' excuse for criminal behavior from evolutionary psychologists." Evolution, in addition to being bad science, encourages the dismissal of personal guilt, reducing sinful behavior to mere instinct.

173

Grocery shopping can be enlightening in many ways. While waiting to check out, a shopper can read why someone has a crush on their alien abductor, or loves their talking poodle's poetry, or enjoys daily encounters with Elvis. Tabloid papers thrive on wild headlines. Some people find them believable, while others laugh. Interestingly, a report on several surveys found that compared to irreligious college students, evangelical Christians were far less likely to believe in superstitions such as ghosts, palm readers, and psychics.[1] That's likely one reason evangelicals generally avoid tabloid-style stories.

Tabloid journalism isn't alone in supplying dubious or salacious stories. Consider headlines based on evolutionary psychology regarding why certain behaviors happen: "It's evolution: Nature of prejudice, aggression different for men and women"; "Some STIs Are Beneficial, and May Have Boosted Evolutionary Promiscuity"; "There's an Evolutionary Reason Guys Like Curves"; "Female animals look drab to avoid sexual harassment, study shows"; "How make-up makes men admire but other women jealous"; "Does Postpartum Depression Serve an Evolutionary Purpose?"; "Whether It's a Peacock Or a Porsche, Men Like to Show Off, Study Finds"; "Lady Liaisons: Does Cheating Give Females an Evolutionary Advantage? A 17-year-long study upends the most common evolutionary explanation of female infidelity."

Can these stories be taken seriously? Or are they another major evolutionary blunder that, in this case, should be laughed off just like tabloid-style headlines?

Evolutionary psychology explains human behavior as a legacy of preprogrammed adaptive actions that emerged from our struggle to survive. It applies evolutionary biology to daily living. However, does either field have scientific merit? The opinion among evolutionists is split. One study advocating for indoctrinating medical students with evolution claims that "evolutionary biology is a unifying principle that provides a framework for organizing medical knowledge from other basic sciences."[2]

Yet, evolutionary authority Jerry Coyne disagrees. He says:

In science's pecking order, evolutionary biology lurks somewhere near the bottom, far closer to phrenology than to physics. For evolutionary biology is a historical science, laden with history's inevitable imponderables....The latest deadweight dragging us closer to phrenology is "evolutionary psychology," or the science formerly known as sociobiology, which studies the evolutionary roots of human behavior.[3]

Determining who's right requires some knowledge of evolutionary psychology. Does this field prompt the kind of vivid imagination aligned with Darwin's look-imagine-see explanatory method?[4] If so, then evolutionary psychologists may be prone to embrace mystical explanations in which nature exercises agency over creatures to shape their behaviors as well as their physical forms.

Evolutionary Psychology Sees Behavior as Survival Adaptations

The belief that behaviors result from evolutionary adaptation is fundamental. Per Mary Jane West-Eberhard, "The use of 'adaptation' by evolutionary biologists" differs from other biologists. "To be considered an adaptation a trait must be shown to be a consequence of selection for that trait" in "what Darwin called 'the struggle for existence.'"[5]

Thus, specific behaviors previously believed to be vital for survival now function in us more like instincts.

Evolutionary psychology rests on several key premises.... The first premise states that the complexity of human behavior can only be understood by taking into account human evolutionary history and natural selection. Second, behavior depends on *evolved psychological mechanisms.* These... process specific information and generate as output specific behaviors....Third, evolved psychological mechanisms are functionally specialized to perform a specific task....Finally, the *numerousness* premise states that human brains consist of many specific evolved psychological mechanisms that work together to produce behavior.[6]

The study containing the above insight clarifies that though evolutionary psychologists "often frame hypotheses in terms of the costs and benefits to an organism of performing a particular behavior," that "these terms carry no moral or ethical meaning and are used only in terms of naturally selected biological functioning."[6]

Evolutionary Psychology Projects Animal Behavior on Humans

Evolutionary psychologists definitely use Darwin's practice of look-imagine-see methodology. Researchers observe similar animal and human behaviors, then study animal interrelationships to make their best guess about why their behaviors happen, and finally project that explanation onto humans.

This projection links animal actions with what is thought to be instinctive human behavior. One BBC story, "Why bullying is such a successful evolutionary strategy," states: "It is not just people that bully the vulnerable. Many animals do it too, and in evolutionary terms it may even work."[7] That article notes bullying behavior among birds, fish, hyenas, and especially the primates. After observing this similarity, the search for an evolution-based motive starts.

[The chimp's bullying actions] suggest that bullying your way to the top has a long history, and may even be innate.... "Chimps are 'natural bullies' and I have seen it often," says Richard Wrangham of Harvard University....In fact, [bullying] is often unprovoked, says Dario Maestripieri of the University of Chicago, Illinois. "Dominants attack subordinates out of the blue, for no apparent reason." This unsolicited harassment may serve a useful purpose. Maestripieri argues that bullying helps dominant animals to intimidate their subordinates, and that this has clear evolutionary benefits. It ensures that the dominant individuals have better access to food and to the opposite sex. "The more a female is bullied by a particular male, the more that male gets to mate her. Sad but true," says Wrangham.[7]

Finally, a projection to instinctive human behavior happens.

This seems to suggest a bleak conclusion. If so many creatures bully, perhaps bullying is innate in us, something we cannot escape...."Human bullying is both the product of tendencies inherited from our chimp-like ancestors, and of competitive social environments like those of chimps and rhesus monkeys," says Maestripieri.[7]

If our behaviors spring from evolved psychological instincts, then what does this indicate about the human will? Only the boldest advocates of evolutionary psychology publicly state the logical implication—that we actually have no choice in how we act.

Free Will vs. Evolutionarily Inherited Compulsory Behavior

Evolutionist William Provine, the late Cornell professor and author of the essay "No Free Will," astutely understood the clash of evolutionary ideas with God's revelation-based behaviors. In a recap of his interview with Provine, one journalist wrote, "With the destruction of the argument for design, there is no going back to a world in which our ethics can be based on a revelation of what God demands of us."[8] He added:

Nor can we reasonably expect people to behave morally by exercising free will, because free will simply doesn't exist. Genetics and environmental factors do not merely influence our moral decisions—they determine them....Free will, Provine argues, is not simply a myth. "It is a destructive myth, one of the meanest, nastiest, most divisive ideas we've developed in all our cultural history. We use it," he says, "to blame people for their actions and to justify mistreating [i.e., punitively incarcerating] people."[8]

Thus, evolutionary psychologists suggest that a human's unconscious reactions—not choices—are practically inevitable, even when destructive.

In her catalog of published evolutionary psychological theories, Denyse O'Leary sums up how they explain all, even contradictory, behaviors "that are now assumed to be encoded in our genes through natural selection. Thus our brains enact programs whose true nature we do not understand. But the evolutionary psychologist does."[9] She elaborates how:

> This encoded behaviour can be shopping, voting, or tipping at restaurants. It can also be: Why children don't like vegetables (nothing to do with young 'uns preference for sweet things); why hungry men prefer plump women (not just because they probably know where the kitchen is); why we have color vision (mainly to detect blushing); why we are sexually jealous (not fear of abandonment, but "sperm competition"); why toddlers are Neanderthals (not just immature); why we don't stick to our goals (evolution gave us a kludge brain); why women prefer men with stubble (except for those who don't); why gossip is good for you (despite wrecked relationships)....[9]

And on goes her intriguing litany of our presumed compulsory behaviors.

Uh-Oh…Evolutionary Psychologists Explain Rape

Evolutionists tolerate evolved psychological mechanisms that compel us to, say, shop for shoes. But some people revolt when these mechanisms are used to explain humans shopping for mates, or worse, of men shopping for women who aren't on the market. In 2000, MIT Press published *A Natural History of Rape: Biological Bases of Sexual Coercion*.[10] A furor arose over the way this book applies evolutionary psychology to rape.

One backlash was over people who seem to mitigate rape's moral dimension. The authors envisioned nature as beneficially selecting behaviors that bypass free will and simply "happen."

In response to the backlash, the authors amended their book's preface. They state, "There is no connection here between what is biological or naturally selected and what is morally right or wrong."[11] Their conclusion for rape itself remained divisive even in the amended preface.

We argue that a *desire for sexual stimulation*, not a desire to produce offspring, is a proximate cause of raping and is the common denominator across human rapes of all kinds. Men's sexual ardor is, in ultimate terms, a product of past selection pressure that favored it because it increased sexual access to many females of reproductive age....Women are evolved to choose mates carefully....Rape is one of the many behaviors that result from this evolved difference in male and female sexuality.[12]

Other evolutionary psychologists agree that rape is a selected adaptation.

For rape to be produced by evolved psychological mechanisms, it must have recurrently generated reproductive benefits for ancestral rapists....There is evidence that rape may have increased the number of women with whom ancestral men copulated and, therefore, the reproductive success of rapist males.[13]

"And that is why we carry rape genes today. The family trees of prehistoric men lacking rape genes petered out," reports science writer Sharon Begley. She lampoons evolution-based stories explaining men's behavior and women's looks. "Men attracted to young, curvaceous babes were fitter because such women were the most fertile; mating with dumpy, barren hags is not a good way to grow a big family tree."[14]

Naturalists claim to love science, but they hate science when evolutionary models deliver undesirable conclusions. Applying evolution to rape wasn't controversial, but concluding that rape happened "for sexual stimulation" was. This claim was taken to be anti-feminist per "'gender feminism': feminism that is based on inter-gender conflict, with virtually all that is male denounced as domineering, evil, untrustworthy, out-group, and enemy."[15] Gender feminists declare that male-over-female domination motivates rape, not sexual gratification. These evolutionary psychologists threatened feminism's view, and they furthered the angst by adding, "That a woman's manner of dress may affect her risk of rape is eminently reasonable in view of what is known about certain sexual adaptations of men."[15]

Evolutionist Critics of Evolutionary Psychology Indict Themselves

Begley reports:

Over the years [evolutionary psychology] arguments have attracted legions of critics who thought the science was weak and the message (what philosopher David Buller of Northern Illinois University called "a get-out-of-jail-free card" for heinous behavior) pernicious. But the reaction to the rape book was of a whole different order. Biologist Joan Roughgarden of Stanford University called it "the latest 'evolution made me do it' excuse for criminal behavior from evolutionary psychologists."[16]

"Weak science" criticisms center on non-testable claims that a maladaptive behavior today like rape was once a useful adaptive behavior. But how does one know if a behavior is truly an adaptation or rather some non-adaptable trait that simply tagged along?

Coyne seized on this ambiguity. "In keeping with the traditions established early in the evolution of sociobiology, [*A Natural History of Rape*'s] evidence comes down to a series of untestable 'just-so' stories."[17] Elsewhere, he says:

The problem is that evolutionary psychology suffers from the scientific equivalent of megalomania. Most of its adherents are convinced that virtually every human action or feeling, including depression, homosexuality, religion, and consciousness, was put directly into our brains by natural selection....Unlike bones, behavior does not fossilize, and understanding its evolution often involves concocting stories that sound plausible but are hard to test.[18]

However, when it serves him Coyne makes the same Darwinian claim. "The theory of natural selection has a big job— the biggest in biology. Its task is to explain how every adaptation evolved...not just body form....Selection has to explain behaviors, both cooperative and antagonistic."[19] Coyne unwittingly accentuates how ambiguity and "just-so" stories epitomize evolution itself.

Fittingly, in practice "evolutionary psychology is empirically unwarranted and conceptually incoherent to such an extent that it is a matter of professional sociological concern why it has come to achieve such a degree of popularity," concludes the evolutionist who penned "The Darwinian Cage." He alludes to why evolutionists will contentedly live in their cage of imaginative tabloid-style stories. It's not evolution but a compelling "commitment to naturalistic explanation....Since no one wishes to keep company with the creationists, the evolutionary psychological programme [*sic*] appears irresistible."[20]

Biblical truth exposes evolutionary psychology as futile

and blame-shifting "evolution made me do it" stories as foolish. "The heart is deceitful above all things, and desperately wicked; who can know it? I, the LORD, search the heart, I test the mind, even to give every man according to his ways, according to the fruit of his doings" (Jeremiah 17:9-10).

References
1. Hemingway, M. Z. Look Who's Irrational Now. *The Wall Street Journal*. Posted on wsj.com September 19, 2008, accessed November 18, 2016.
2. Nesse, R. M. et al. 2010. Making evolutionary biology a basic science for medicine. *Proceedings of the National Academy of Sciences*. 107 (suppl 1): 1800-1807.
3. Coyne, J. A. Of Vice and Men—The Fairy Tales of Evolutionary Psychology. Printed in *The New Republic* April 3, 2000, reposted on business.highbeam.com, accessed November 11, 2016.
4. Guliuzza, R. 2016. Major Evolutionary Blunders: Haeckel's Embryos Born of Evolutionary Imagination. *Acts & Facts*. 45 (11): 16-18.
5. West-Eberhard, M. J. 1992. Adaptation: Current Usages. In *Keywords in Evolutionary Biology*. E. F. Keller and E. A. Lloyd, eds. Cambridge, MA: Harvard University Press, 13.
6. McKibbin, W. F. et al. 2008. Why Do Men Rape? An Evolutionary Psychological Perspective. *Review of General Psychology*. 12 (1): 86-97. Emphasis in original.
7. Hogenboom, M. Why bullying is such a successful evolutionary strategy. *BBC Earth*. Posted on bbc.com August 23, 2016, accessed November 11, 2016.
8. Liles, G. The Faith of an Atheist. *MD*. March 1994, 59-64.
9. O'Leary, D. Dissecting the caveman theory of psychology. MercatorNet. Posted on mercatornet. com August 10, 2009, accessed November 12, 2016.
10. Thornhill, R. and C. T. Palmer. 2000. *A Natural History of Rape: Biological Bases of Sexual Coercion*. Cambridge, MA: MIT Press.
11. Thornhill, R. and C. T. Palmer. 2002. *Rape and Evolution: A Reply to Our Critics*. Psychology *Evolution & Gender*. 4 (3): 283-296.
12. Ibid, emphasis added.
13. McKibbin, Why Do Men Rape?, 88.
14. Begley, S. Can We Blame Our Bad Behavior on Stone-Age Genes? *Newsweek*. Posted on newsweek.com June 19, 2009, accessed on November 12, 2016.
15. Thornhill, *Rape and Evolution*, 12.
16. Begley, Can We Blame Our Bad Behavior on Stone-Age Genes?
17. Coyne, J. A. and A. Berry. 2000. Rape as an adaptation. *Nature*. 404 (6774): 121-122.
18. Coyne, Of Vice and Men.
19. Coyne, J. A. 2009. *Why Evolution Is True*. New York: Viking, 119. Emphasis in original.
20. Hamilton, R. 2008. The Darwinian Cage: Evolutionary Psychology as Moral Science. *Theory, Culture & Society*. 25 (2): 105-125.

18

Convergent Evolution Is a Seductive Intellectual Swindle

Summary

Totally different kinds of creatures often share similar features. Evolutionists frequently explain these similarities with *convergent evolution.* This imaginative idea states that creatures on different ancestral branches somehow evolved similar traits. An example might be two cacti that are genetically distinct, but physically indistinguishable. One of the many problems with this speculation is that it supposes that complex features evolved separately multiple times. Eyes, with their astonishing complexity, are believed to have evolved independently up to 65 different times! And for similar creatures, this happened with all their organs and features. As two intelligent design researchers summed up, "Without some form of design or teleological guidance, convergent evolution requires a piling of coincidences upon coincidences that strains credulity." Evolutionists have started to recognize the incredible implausibility of convergent evolution, but they fail to recognize the hand of the Creator.

When it comes to swindles, it would be hard to top Liz Carmichael. She spun a tale about obtaining proprietary secrets from her deceased NASA engineer husband that enabled her to start and become CEO of a totally bogus car company marketing the Dale. This fictitious 84 mpg, three-wheeled car bilked millions from investors in 1975…and all the while Liz was actually a man, Jerry Dean Michael, impeccably dressed like a woman. No investor ever saw the car factory or drove a Dale. Yet, "Liz" always talked with investors so matter-of-factly about "her" wholly imaginary industrial realm that they willingly visualized everything within their hopeful minds, where it took on a vivid life of its own.

An intellectual swindle rivaling this is the wholly imaginary fabrication called *convergent evolution*—the idea that the same traits evolved independently in completely different organisms. Like "Liz's" investment pitch, evolutionists also write about it so matter-of-factly that it has taken on a genuine life of its own in their willing minds. Why do they embrace convergent evolution so eagerly? Because it serves as a rescuing device for an important dogma of evolutionary theory. (A rescuing device is a completely fabricated conjecture devised to save someone's theory from contrary evidence.)

Evolutionary theory holds that physical features shared by different creatures are strong evidence for evolution. To evolutionists, common traits are best explained by their descent from a common ancestor—not by shared common design. Darwin taught:

All the…difficulties with classification are explained, if I do not greatly deceive myself, on the view that the natural system is founded in descent with modification: that the characters which the naturalists consider as showing true affinity between any two or more species, are those which have been inherited from a common parent…that community of descent is the hidden bond which naturalists have been unconsciously seeking, and not some unknown plan of creation.[1]

However, this highly revered tenet greatly needs rescuing because so many nonhereditary similarities contradict it. Convergent evolution is the fabricated conjecture evolutionists invoke to explain very similar characteristics between creatures that could not have been inherited from a common ancestor. But evolutionists will never accept them as having been produced by an intelligently designed internal programming that is specified for common purposes.

Evolutionary literature often contracts convergent evolution down to its central idea and simply calls it *convergence*.

The Basic Notion of Convergence Is Imaginary

It is tempting to start an evaluation of convergent evolution by identifying all its problems. This is where a word of caution is necessary. Like other key elements of evolutionary theory, convergence is *not* an observable process but only exists in someone's mind. Convergence is another evolutionary mystical, mental construct.

We should not naively proceed into matter-of-fact discussions of convergence without questioning the basic premise that such a Darwinian process truly happened. If we don't question it, we give convergence a life of its own—just like "Liz" got her investors to hand over their money for an imaginary product and thus perpetuated the misleading of other people. It is better to begin by rejecting the idea that convergence accurately explains *any* historical realities and then show that fanciful narratives about convergence amount to *ad hoc*, just-so stories.

A Magical Story Substitutes for Purposeful Internal Programming

In *Why Evolution Is True*, Jerry Coyne explains convergence by describing two similar-looking but unrelated cacti: "I have both types growing on my windowsill, and visitors can't tell them apart without reading their tags."[2] He knows that common ancestry cannot explain their similarity, so he focuses on eliminating the explanation that their shared traits result from designed internal programming for common purposes. Switching from science to theology, Coyne asks:

> Why would a creator put plants that are fundamentally different, but look so similar, in diverse areas of the world that seem ecologically identical? Wouldn't it make more sense to put the same species of plants in areas with the same type of soil and climate?[2]

By answering his own question with an "*I* wouldn't do it that way" reply, Coyne dismisses any consideration of design—a classic evolutionary tactic. He thus dodges thoughtful discussion of possible design-based explanations.

Coyne also substitutes what he believes is a "well-known"—i.e., matter-of-fact—scientific alternative in lieu of designed internal programming. Yet, he merely invokes a simple magical story that is not based on fact but only exists in his mind.

Again one must ask: If animals were specially created, why would the creator produce on different continents fundamentally different animals that nevertheless look and act so much alike?...No creationist, whether of the Noah's Ark variety or otherwise, has offered a credible explanation for why different types of animals have similar forms in different places. All they can do is invoke the inscrutable whims of the creator. But evolution *does* explain the pattern by invoking a well-known process called *convergent evolution.* It's really quite simple. Species that live in similar habitats will experience similar selection pressures from their environment, so they may evolve similar adaptations, or converge, coming to look and behave very much alike even though they are unrelated.[2]

Another evolutionary authority, the late Ernst Mayr of Harvard, claimed convergence illustrates how evolution functions as a substitute "engineer": "Convergence illustrates beautifully how selection is able to make use of the intrinsic variability of organisms to engineer adapted types for almost any kind of environmental niche."[3] Evolution is thus the "intrinsic variability," or a creature's normal heterozygosity, coupled with the natural process of struggling to live that fractionates the diverse alleles into various populations.

Casually Invoking Convergent Evolution Everywhere

Evolutionary literature projects engineering prowess and God-like volition onto unconscious nature and weaves an active nature-agent into its narratives.[4] This helps the incredible accomplishments claimed for evolution appear more believable. Ascribing the ability for nature to repeatedly converge on the same trait in very diverse organisms—sometimes separated by many millions of years, even to identical genes—gives convergent evolution a seemingly omnipotent capability.

For evolutionists, convergence's supreme power is both implicit and pervasive. A belief expressed in a study published in *Nature* "hints that evolution may be finding the same genetic solutions to a problem more often than previously thought" and "that convergent molecular evolution is much more widespread than previously recognized."[5]

Convergent evolution is casually used to explain an enormous litany of complicated biological traits. A few examples from evolutionary literature will highlight some of the capabilities ascribed to convergence.

For instance, the power of convergence is projected in extinct wildebeest-like mammals that had trumpet-like nasal passages remarkably like the nasal crests of hadrosaur dinosaurs—even though both were allegedly separated by millions of years. By casually explaining this anatomical similarity by convergence, evolutionists morph it into wondrous evidence for evolution.

The fossil record provides tangible, historical evidence for the mode and operation of evolution across deep time. Striking patterns of convergence are some of the strongest examples of these operations, whereby, over time, similar environmental and/or behavioral pressures precipitate similarity in form and function between disparately related taxa.[6]

The precision of convergence is seen in finding out that 59 swimming or flying animal species ranging from mollusks to insects, birds, bats, whales, and fish all use the same fluid motion mechanics. The tips of their wings, fins, etc. all bend at essentially the same point and flex 26 degrees. The research team pondered, "What factor(s) drive natural selection to converge on highly constrained bending kinematics across such a wide range of animal groups?"[7] They speculated that nature molded these diverse organisms as it drove them independently through time in the quest for energy efficiency.

The scope of convergence is seen in multitudes of organisms evolving eyes. Evolutionists claim that similar environments constrained creatures to converge on comparably complex eyes—independently at least 40 times, and probably as many as 65 times.[8]

But even if claims of Darwinian convergence were not *ad hoc* stories, the concept still has serious problems.

Problem 1: Imagining Coincidence upon Coincidence

Developmental biologist Sean Carroll reports that a similar gene, *Pax-6*, "has been found to be associated with eye formation in animals with all sorts of eyes." Convergence is normally the explanation of choice for these similarities. But Carroll rejects convergence as implausible since that account simply invokes "a remarkable coincidence in that the *Pax-6* gene was called upon repeatedly to build eyes from scratch in these different groups of animals."[9] Instead of convergence, he embraces another imaginary account that is equally implausible. He believes these genes were remarkably conserved and went unchanged for 600 million years in organisms as diverse as flies and elephants. But other genes became so mutated and different from each other that they caused the evolution of flies and elephants.

Carroll's "remarkable coincidence" is exceedingly restrained. Similarities of marsupial and placental mammals are presented as another showpiece of convergence. Evolutionists believe that on Australia and the Americas, nearly identical environmental conditions—drought, flood, heat wave, Ice Age, famine, disease, food types, predators—were occurring over vast ages in nearly identical intensity, timing, sequence, and other factors to mold not just *a gene* but whole suites of physiological and anatomical features to coincidently arrive at remarkably similar body types for dogs, wolves, cats, anteaters, moles, mice, Coyne's cacti, etc. Two intelligent design researchers sum up, "Without some form of design or teleological guidance, convergent evolution requires a piling of coincidences upon coincidences that strains credulity."[10]

Problem 2: Convergent Evolution versus Darwin's "Community of Descent"

Every occasion in which evolutionists must invoke convergence argues against similar features being strong evidence for evolution. When looking at similar features, which evolutionary explanation is legitimate—convergence or common descent? Or should both be taken as imaginary scenarios? Consider a report on unexpected genetic similarities for genes enabling echolocation in whales and bats.

The discovery represents an unprecedented example of adaptive sequence convergence between two highly divergent groups....[Study author Stephen Rossiter said,] "It is generally assumed that most of these so-called convergent traits have arisen by different genes or different mutations. Our study shows that a complex trait—echolocation—has in fact evolved by identical genetic changes in bats and dolphins....We were surprised by...the sheer number of convergent changes in the coding DNA."[11]

The same report stated:

If you draw a phylogenetic [relationship] tree of bats, whales, and a few other mammals based on similarities in the prestin [a hearing gene] sequence alone, the echolocating bats and whales come out together rather than with their rightful evolutionary cousins.[11]

Addressing this specific contradiction, Lee Spetner perceptively observes:

Convergent evolution is...an invention. It was invented solely to avoid addressing the failure of the phylogenetic tree to support Common Descent. There is no theoretical support for convergence, and whatever evidence has been given for it is the product of a circular argument.[12]

The blunder of evolutionary theory is that similar features are evidence for evolution...except when they aren't.

Problem 3: Convergent Evolution Was "Stunningly" Wrong

What about teaching 40 independent evolutionary developments of various eyes? That manifested into another incredible evolutionary blunder. "This view was entirely incorrect," Sean Carroll notes after citing genes called *Hox genes* that control eye development in sighted creatures. "The late Stephen Jay

Gould...saw the discovery of *Hox* clusters...as overturning a major view of the Modern Synthesis [natural selection fractioning out genetic variability]." Carroll candidly continues, "Natural selection has not forged many eyes completely from scratch; there is a common genetic ingredient to making each eye type, as well as to the many types of appendages, hearts, etc."[13]

A Better Organism-Focused, Design-Based Explanation

The general evolutionary view is bankrupt. It states that nature acts as an exercising agency to mold passive organisms into unlimited forms as they are driven by environmental challenges called *selective pressures*. Convergence is not an observation that flows from objectively discernible causes but is a declaration based on mental pictures—a metaphysical conjecture that substitutes for a total absence of an explanation.

However, creationists have long stated that similar traits in diverse creatures function toward similar purposes. They expected to find shared genetic programming to guide the traits' development, an expectation confirmed in *Hox* genes, gene networks, and other mechanisms.[14]

In a recent rebuff to convergence, ICR geneticist Dr. Jeffrey Tomkins discussed how pythons and boas can each express—evidently quite quickly—some highly similar yet environmentally specific traits that enable them to fit and fill different niches.[15]

These findings tend to confirm design-based creationist theory that emphasizes active, problem-solving organisms that are capable of extraordinary self-adjustments to fill dynamic environments. Future research will likely confirm more details of how creatures can detect signals during development (and also afterward) and make self-adjustments to their own traits per internal algorithms. Sensors, algorithms, and other internal system elements enable them to actively and continuously track environmental changes—not be passively molded by them.

Such extreme bioengineering magnifies the profound wisdom of nature's true creative Agent, the Lord Jesus Christ (Psalm 104:24).

References

1. Darwin, C. 1872. *On the Origin of Species by Means of Natural Selection,* 6th ed. London: John Murray, 369.
2. Coyne, J. 2009. *Why Evolution Is True.* New York: Viking, 91-94. Emphasis in original.
3. Mayr, E. 2001. *What Evolution Is.* New York: Basic Books, 223.
4. Biello, D. Was Darwin a Punk? *Scientific American.* Posted on scientificamerican.com September 28, 2010, accessed January 3, 2017. See also Guliuzza, R. 2014. A Response to "Does Natural Selection Exist?" *Answers Research Journal.* 7: 403-420.
5. Hayden, E. C. Convergent evolution seen in hundreds of genes. *Nature News.* Posted on nature.com September 4, 2013, accessed January 1, 2017.
6. O'Brien, H. D. et al. 2016. Unexpected Convergent Evolution of Nasal Domes between Pleistocene Bovids and Cretaceous Hadrosaur Dinosaurs. *Current Biology.* 26 (4): 503-508.
7. Lucas, K. N. et al. 2014. Bending rules for animal propulsion. *Nature Communications.* 5: 3293.
8. Land, M. F. and R. D. Fernald. 1992. The Evolution of Eyes. *Annual Review of Neuroscience.* 15: 1-29, referencing Salvini-Plawen, L. V. and E. Mayr. 1977. On the evolution of photoreceptors and eyes. *Evolutionary Biology.* 10: 207-263.
9. Carroll, S. B. 2005. *Endless Forms Most Beautiful.* New York: W. W. Norton, 68-69.
10. Dembski, W. A. and J. Wells. 2008. *The Design of Life.* Dallas: The Foundation for Thought and Ethics, 116.
11. Cell Press. In bats and whales, convergence in echolocation ability runs deep. *ScienceDaily.* Posted on sciencedaily.com January 27, 2010, accessed January 1, 2017.
12. Spetner, L. M. 2014. *The Evolution Revolution: Why Thinking People Are Rethinking the Theory of Evolution.* New York: Judaica Press, Kindle Locations 1229-1231.
13. Carroll, *Endless Forms Most Beautiful,* 72.
14. Guliuzza, R. J. 2015. Major Evolutionary Blunders: Evolutionary Predictions Fail the Reality Test. *Acts & Facts.* 44 (9): 17-19.
15. Tomkins, J. P. Convergent Evolution or Design-Based Adaptation? *Creation Science Update.* Posted on ICR.org July 7, 2016, accessed January 2, 2017.

19

Evolutionists Falsely Predict "Junk DNA"

Summary

To evolutionists, nature is a mindless tinkerer driving the evolutionary process in fits and starts down a meandering path throughout Earth's history. Just like they expect the human body to have "vestigial organs," they also expect the human genome to have many useless sequences. They call this *junk DNA*. It was widely touted as definitive evidence of our evolutionary ancestry. Even prominent Christians used it to argue for evolution. When the Human Genome Project was published in 2001, evolutionists quickly labeled 95% of it "junk DNA." Creationists cautioned that the "junk" label was premature and could hinder research. Yet, several leading evolutionists believed the genetic "junk" was unlikely to have any function, and "that it would be folly in such cases to hunt obsessively for one." However, contrary to secular expectations, new research is completely turning those tables and finding a large amount of function.

The suspense is palpable as fans watch baseball slugger Casey at the plate primed to wallop a game-winning home run. "And now the pitcher holds the ball, and now he lets it go, and now the air is shattered by the force of Casey's blow." But the blow turns out to be a massive swing-and-a-miss for Casey—a total whiff—so "there is no joy in Mudville—mighty Casey has struck out."[1] Ernest Thayer's legendary 1888 baseball poem conveys the message of how overblown expectations, bolstered by smug overconfidence, can be dashed when the actual performance results in an enormous swing-and-a-miss.

Just like the mighty but futile force of "Casey's blow," evolutionary literature gloated for over three decades about evidence evolutionists believed was a powerful confirmation of evolution. Their "proof" was the discovery that a large percentage of DNA they called *junk DNA* does not code for proteins. Since evolutionists believe that over long ages organisms (and their DNA) are crafted by chaotic environments in which they struggle to survive, evolutionists expect to see in evolution's wake many different types of "useless" genetic junk. They were so certain that most non-coding genetic material was junk DNA, some said its only functional ability was embarrassing creationists.

Yet, joyless Mudville was let down by Casey, and recently there has been less joy in Evolutionville as the expectations of junk DNA have been exposed as overblown. Thoughtful research confirmed function for much of the diverse types of DNA mislabeled as junk. Scientific evidence showed the widely touted "junk DNA" argument, which evolutionists anticipated being a Darwinian home run, is really a blundering swing-and-a-miss—another total whiff—for their theory.

Evolutionary Theory Expects to Find Genetic Junk in Organisms

Evolutionary proponents have had many whiffs. Recall the case of Haeckel's embryos, which were touted as reflecting the stages of organisms' evolutionary past. Biochemist Michael Behe noted, "The story of the embryos is an object lesson in seeing what you want to see."[2]

And regarding the Piltdown Man hoax, biology philosopher Jane Maienschein recounted "how easily susceptible researchers can be manipulated into believing that they have actually found just what they had been looking for."[3] These episodes and others show that rather than being established by observation and experiment, major evidences for evolution have historically only needed to be phenomena that could be envisioned within evolutionary scenarios. Thus, finding DNA that does not code for protein, or looks like genetic wreckage, or appears as a hodgepodge of non-functional genetic repeats, etc., matches the chaotic genetic history of life on Earth that an evolutionary theorist is expecting to see in DNA.

This evolutionary "sight" affects all levels of scientific interpretation. Scientists whose analysis is constrained to fit evolutionary theory will not see a brain, a digestive system, and other complicated biological phenomena as designed things but rather as conglomerations of parts cobbled together by nature. "We're all here because of mutations," claims molecular neuroscience professor Jernej Ule, who adds:

But most random mutations actually disrupt the functions of our genes and so are a common source of genetic diseases....

How does nature resolve this conflict?...We've known for decades that evolution needs to tinker with genetic elements so they can accumulate mutations while minimising [*sic*] disruption to the fitness of a species.[4]

How can Ule so easily embrace such counterintuitive thinking? By using a mental rescuing device. He believes that a simple appeal to nature is a sufficient stand-alone cause to explain phenomena that in any field other than biology would require the actions of an intelligent agent. Ule conceives of nature as being like an omnipotent agent capable of "resolving conflict" and "tinkering" with organisms over time. Nature, just like a potter, thus fashions creatures as if they were modeling clay.

This belief is widespread because most research programs in Ule's field of evolutionary biology are shaped by a very influential concept synopsized in Nobel laureate Francois Jacob's 1977 paper "Evolution and Tinkering."[5] Nature was described as a mindless tinkerer that drove the evolutionary process in fits and starts, down dead ends, in U-turns and other meandering paths throughout Earth's history. Evolutionists believe that numerous "mistakes" and "junk" in living things confirm that nature started with a primitive cell and shaped it into all of life's diverse forms. For them, the perceived struggle to survive explains why biology has both junk and incredibly complicated molecular machines that look like they were designed for a purpose—but really weren't.

The distinguished biochemical researcher Walter Neupert explains how he and most biologists project God-like powers onto Mother Nature to mentally reconcile the counterintuitive notion that no designer was necessary for living things that look remarkably designed:

> The vast majority of biologists believe that these 'machines' are not made by optimizing a design. Rather, we are convinced that they are the products of aeons of evolutionary processes. Francois Jacob made this clear almost 30 years ago: nature is not an engineer; she is a tinkerer (Jacob, 1977). Molecular machines, although it often may seem so, are not made with a blueprint at hand....There are no blueprints; the workshop of the tinkerer is a collection of millions of bits and pieces that are combined, and odds and ends are used over and over again to yield something that works better.[6]

A more recent scientific article presented a model for a natural origin of microscopic biological machines. Just like Neupert, the evolutionist authors project God-like creative powers onto nature as a whimsical tinkerer: "This model agrees with Jacob's proposition of evolution as a 'tinkerer,' building new machines from salvaged parts."[7] If readers are attuned to it, they will find that evolutionary literature commonly invokes the personification of nature exercising agency through evolution as a substitute for God's intelligent agency. Junk DNA fits perfectly with the evolutionary expectation of biology being messy rather than neatly engineered—and in their minds, evolutionists could "see" junk all over the genome.

Is Junk DNA Strong Evidence for Evolution and against Creation?

The concept of junk DNA began in the early 1970s when genetic researchers made the curious finding that over 95% of

201

DNA does *not* code for proteins. Some DNA is characterized in perplexing ways such as long strings of repeated code that almost seemed like gibberish. Evolutionary researchers believed they were observing genetic fossils and other genetic wreckage left over from nature's tinkering. In reports that were uncharacteristic of good science, many investigators hastily labeled the huge segment of DNA with yet-unknown functions as "junk," beginning with geneticist Susumu Ohno who explained:

> More than 90% degeneracy contained within our genome should be kept in mind when we consider evolutionary changes in genome sizes. What is the reason behind this degeneracy?...The earth is strewn with fossil remains of extinct species; is it a wonder that our genome too is filled with the remains of extinct genes?...Triumphs as well as failures of nature's past experiments appear to be contained in our genome.[8]

Evolutionary authority Jerry Coyne made a post-hoc prediction in 2009 that evolutionists would expect to find DNA in genomes along the lines of Ohno's "junk," and "the evolutionary prediction...has been fulfilled amply." He noted, "Now that we can read DNA sequences directly, we find...in [species] genomes is inscribed much of their evolutionary history, including the wrecks of genes that were once useful."[9]

Junk DNA flourished in evolutionary literature as valid proof of evolution. Evolutionary spokesmen like Ernst Mayr and Richard Dawkins appealed to it. Dawkins claimed that "[pseudogenes] are genes that once did something useful but have now been sidelined and are never transcribed or translated....What pseudogenes are useful for is embarrassing creationists...[since it] is a remarkable fact that the greater part (95 per cent in the case of humans) of the genome might as well not be there, for all the difference it makes."[10]

On one side of the coin, the supposed existence of junk DNA is used as evidence for its evolutionary origin. But as Dawkins implies, on the other side of the coin evolutionists see it as a strong argument against DNA being intelligently designed. Popular science historian Michael Shermer contrasted these two explanations for DNA's origin. "Rather than being intelligently designed," he said, "the human genome looks more and more like a mosaic of mutations, fragmented copies, borrowed sequences, and discarded strings of DNA that were jerry-built over millions of years of evolution."[11] Shermer's comments were consistent with what the evolutionary community was publishing about other genetic research.

In 2001, when the first drafts of the Human Genome Project were published, results were interpreted by some who saw so much "junk" that to them the reality of evolution became a mental certainty.

They identified thousands of segments that had the hallmarks of dead genes. They found transposable elements by the millions. The Human Genome Project team declared that our DNA consisted of isolated oases of protein-coding genes surrounded by "vast expanses of unpopulated desert where only noncoding 'junk' DNA can be found." Junk DNA had started out as a theoretical argument, but now the messiness of our evolution was laid bare for all to see.[12]

Collins Fits Junk DNA into Theistic Evolution

Geneticist Francis Collins was the Director of the Human Genome Project and currently is Director of the National Institutes of Health. Unsurprisingly, he once endorsed the concept of junk DNA. What did surprise many was the degree to which Collins publicly identified his work as fully compatible with belief in God's creative agency. He was instrumental in founding the organization BioLogos to promote evolutionary creationism. BioLogos credits the diversity of life on Earth to "the God-ordained process of evolution"[13]—i.e., theistic evolution, in which natural or created heterozygosity (genetic diversity) is fractionated out by natural processes. Citing junk DNA as evidence for evolution, Collins said:

> Even more compelling evidence for a common ancestor comes from the study of what are known as ancient repetitive elements (AREs)....Mammalian genomes are littered with such AREs, with roughly 45 percent of the human genome made up of such genetic flotsam and jetsam.[14]

Within the same context, he mocked creationists who claimed from an investigative standpoint that the "junk DNA" label was premature: "Of course, some might argue that these are actually functional elements placed there by a Creator for a good reason, and our discounting them as 'junk DNA' just betrays our current level of ignorance."[14]

Creationists at the time were adamant that experiments had not ruled out a functional role for this DNA. They disagreed that it should be classified as junk given the normal understanding of the word. Bypassing decades of potential research on this DNA, evolutionary authorities simply declared it "junk." In fact, two leading researchers had already concluded by 1980 that "the conviction has been growing that much of this extra DNA is 'junk,'" unlikely to have any function and "that it would be folly in such cases to hunt obsessively for one."[15] Consistent with Darwin's look-imagine-see approach to science,[16] it was natural for evolutionary researchers to clearly envision DNA of unknown function as junk given their firm evolutionary beliefs.

However, at the time when junk DNA was being declared as factual evidence for evolution and against creation, there were already published scientific reports on some "junk" DNA that documented its important functions. The next chapter will show that ignoring these findings was akin to the hubris the slugger Casey flaunted just before his embarrassing total whiff of the pitch.

References

1. Thayer, E. Casey at the Bat: A Ballad of the Republic Sung in the Year 1888. *The Daily Examiner,* June 3, 1888.
2. Behe, M. J. Teach Evolution—And Ask Hard Questions. *New York Times.* Posted on nytimes.com August 13, 1999, accessed September 28, 2016. See Guliuzza, R. 2016. Major Evolutionary Blunders: Haeckel's Embryos Born of Evolutionary Imagination. *Acts & Facts.* 45 (11): 16-18.
3. Maienschein, J. 1997. The One and the Many: Epistemological Reflections on the Modern Human Origins Debates. *Conceptual Issues in Modern Human Origins Research.* Clark, G. A. and C. M. Willermet, eds. New York: Aldine de Gruyter, 413. See Guliuzza, R. 2015. Major Evolutionary Blunders: The Imaginary Piltdown Man. *Acts & Facts.* 44 (12): 12-14.
4. Ule, J. Hidden Code in DNA Explains How New Gene Pieces Are Made. *RealClear Science.* Posted on realclearscience.com January 10, 2017, accessed January 11, 2017.
5. Jacob, F. 1977. Evolution and tinkering. *Science.* 196 (4295): 1161-1166
6. Neupert, W. 2005. Highlight: Molecular Machines. *Biological Chemistry.* 386 (8): 711.
7. Clements, A. et al. 2009. The reducible complexity of a mitochondrial molecular machine. *Proceedings of the National Academy of Sciences.* 106 (37): 15791-15795.
8. Ohno, S. 1972. So much "junk" DNA in our genome. *Brookhaven Symposia in Biology.* 23: 366-370. Posted on junkdna.com, accessed December 31, 2015.
9. Coyne, J. 2009. *Why Evolution Is True.* New York: Viking, 67, 56.
10. Dawkins, R. 2009. *The Greatest Show on Earth: The Evidence for Evolution.* New York: Free Press, 332-333.

11. Shermer, M. 2006. *Why Darwin Matters: The Case Against Intelligent Design.* New York: Times-Holt, 75.
12. Zimmer, C. Is Most of Our DNA Garbage? *New York Times.* Posted on nytimes.com March 5, 2015, accessed January 20, 2017.
13. What We Believe. *BioLogos.* Posted on biologos.org.
14. Collins, F. S. 2006. *The Language of God: A Scientist Presents Evidence for Belief.* New York: Free Press, 135-137.
15. Orgel, L. E. and F. H. C. Crick. 1980. Selfish DNA: The Ultimate Parasite. *Nature.* 284 (5757): 606.
16. Guliuzza, Haeckel's Embryos.

20

Evolutionists Dismiss Evidence, Preferring Theory

Summary

Even though evolutionists predicted "junk DNA," new mainstream research crushes that hypothesis. The massive project ENCODE confirmed that 80% of the human genome is functional, and more function is being discovered every day. Evolutionist Francis Collins, director of the National Institutes of Health, says they don't use the term *junk DNA* anymore. He said, "It was pretty much a case of hubris to imagine that we could dispense with any part of the genome—as if we knew enough to say it wasn't functional." Scientific research shows that evolutionary declarations were wrong and creationist predictions were right. However, evolutionary biologists still cling to their dogma, insisting that the analysis must be wrong because it contradicts evolutionary predictions. But ENCODE sticks to its research. One of its geneticists says, "We are far from finished," and that the project could go on endlessly finding function in the human genome. As usual, the more we research creation, the more we find the fingerprints of our Creator.

"Casey at the Bat" is one of America's best-known poems. Surprisingly, even operas have dramatized the story of Mudville Nine's baseball slugger. In Ernest Thayer's 1888 poem, a smugly overconfident Casey was ready to wallop a game-winning home run, only to dash the hopes of Mudville by totally whiffing the ball with a massive—and embarrassing—swing-and-a-miss.

The previous chapter outlined a similar situation for evolutionists.[1] For three decades, they overconfidently declared that the messiness of "junk DNA" confirms how nature exercises creative agency over organisms through evolutionary tinkering. These supposedly useless non-coding bits of genetic sequence were flaunted as leftovers of the evolutionary process. Now we'll see how the true facts about DNA are like a fastball blowing by evolutionists and exposing their overblown claim as a blundering swing-and-a-miss.

Junk DNA Claims Are Stunningly Wrong

Akin to how evolutionists visualized evolutionary characteristics to validate Piltdown Man and vestigial appendixes—characteristics that research has shown only existed in their minds[2]—creationists maintain that hastily labeling any DNA as "junk" is another misguided flight of imagination. In 2006, Human Genome Project Director Francis Collins offered a coy taunt against that view:

> Of course, some might argue that these ["junk DNA" sequences] are actually functional elements placed there by a Creator for a good reason, and our discounting them as "junk DNA" just betrays our current level of ignorance.[3]

His statement proved ironically predictive. By 2015, Collins admitted that a level of ignorance had indeed betrayed the consensus of evolutionists. Numerous discoveries showed functions for DNA once discounted as junk. One science reporter noted:

In January [2015], Francis Collins, the director of the National Institutes of Health, made a comment that revealed just how far the consensus has moved. At a health care conference in San Francisco, an audience member asked him about junk DNA. "We don't use that term anymore," Collins replied. "It was pretty much a case of hubris to imagine that we could dispense with any part of the genome—as if we knew enough to say it wasn't functional." Most of the DNA that scientists once thought was just taking up space in the genome, Collins said, "turns out to be doing stuff."[4]

Reviewing online reports from 1994 until today reveals how espousing notions of junk DNA is simply ill-informed. These carry titles such as "Hidden Treasures in Junk DNA"; "'Junk RNA' molecule found to play key role in cellular response to stress"; "Not 'junk' anymore: Obscure DNA has key role in stroke damage"; "'Junk' All That Separates Humans From Chimps"; "The Unseen Genome: Gems among the Junk"; "Live Chat: New Treasures in the Genome"; "Far From 'Junk,' DNA Dark Matter Proves Crucial to Health"; "Breakthrough study overturns theory of 'junk DNA' in genome."

Thus, for scientists motivated to cure disease, searching DNA for jewels among the "junk" is valuable. Recently, "researchers have shown that when parts of a genome known as enhancers are missing, the heart works abnormally, a finding that bolsters the importance of DNA segments once considered 'junk' because they do not code for specific proteins."[5] And an

MIT report noted that "several years ago, biologists discovered a new type of genetic material known as long noncoding RNA... [in] sections of the genome once believed to be 'junk DNA.' Now, in a related study, biologists have discovered how an enigmatic type of RNA helps to control cell fate."[6]

Once again, research has uncovered newly demonstrated function for biological objects that evolutionists simply declared to be nonfunctional—as if a lack of knowledge of functionality somehow equated to basic evidence that established non-functionality.

Are Tandem Repeats and Pseudogenes Really Junk?

Several reports by ICR geneticist Jeffrey Tomkins cataloged functions for DNA that was considered junk. In regard to repetitive DNA called *tandem repeats* (TRs), Tomkins explained:

Because human reasoning essentially views the repetition of words in spoken languages as errors, these DNA sequences were first written off as meaningless junk....Now it appears nothing could be further from the truth since these repetitive words are linked with pervasive biochemical function.[7]

Tomkins reported on one group of researchers that approached TRs supposing they actually had a purpose. They concluded, "Our results suggest that there are potentially thousands of TR variants in the human genome that exert functional effects via alterations of local gene expression or epigenetics."[8]

Evolutionists have touted *pseudogenes*—supposedly non-functional vestiges of currently functional genes—as junk. Tomkins wrote:

Pseudogenes were once thought to be genomic fossils—the broken remnants of genes that mutated long ago. However, research is progressively showing that many pseudogenes are highly functional and critical to life. Now, a newly characterized pseudogene has been shown to produce a functional protein, but only in cells where it is required—leading researchers to coin a new term *pseudo-pseudogene.*[9]

Tomkins described how the concept of pseudogenes "was based on an over-simplistic view and a lack of advanced information about the complexity of protein production" and "how looking at the genome as a product of evolution hinders scientific discovery."[9]

One massive research project, dubbed ENCODE, examined non-coding DNA for function. Discoveries published in 2012 identified biochemical functions for about 80% of the genome. Tomkins summed up:

Results from 30 simultaneously published high-profile research papers [proclaim] that the human genome is irreducibly complex and intelligently designed. From an evolutionary perspective, this is yet another massive blow to the myth of "Junk DNA." This evolutionary idea was exposed as a fraud from a scientific perspective in Jonathan Well's recent book *The Myth of Junk DNA.*[10]

Further, Tomkins noted, "And what about the remaining 20 percent of the genome—is it functional too?" It's probably not worthless either. Tomkins added that the lead ENCODE analysis coordinator Ewan Birney commented, "It's likely that 80 percent will go to 100 percent....We don't really have any large chunks of redundant DNA. This metaphor of junk isn't that useful."[11]

Rage and Bullying for a Hopeless Cause

Science reporter Carl Zimmer described one scientist's professional reaction to the idea that junk DNA is an invalid concept:

When the N.I.H.'s [National Institutes of Health] official Twitter account relayed Collins's claim about not using the term "junk DNA" anymore, Michael Eisen, a professor at the University of California, Berkeley, tweeted back with a profanity.[12]

The rising tide of public denunciations of the concept of junk DNA by scientists evoked some high-profile anger from a few evolutionary biologists, notably Dan Graur of the University of Houston in Texas, T. Ryan Gregory from the University of Guelph in Ontario, Larry Moran at the University of Toronto, and some others. Zimmer added, "To these biologists, a fully efficient genome would be inconsistent with the arbitrariness of our genesis....Where some look at all those billions of bases and see a finely tuned machine, others, like Gregory, see a disorganized, glorious mess."[12]

Biology declared to be a "glorious mess"—and not neatly designed—is cherished evidence for those who embrace deadly struggles as the fuel for biological change.

Graur understood the negative implications for evolutionary theory if people learned that the idea of junk DNA was an evolutionary swing-and-a-miss. So, he published harsh public attacks against ENCODE research teams in peer-reviewed evolutionary literature. In one paper meant to shame ENCODE researchers into recanting the conclusion that most of the genome had function, he declared:

> This absurd conclusion was reached through various means, chiefly by employing the seldom used "causal role" definition of biological function…by committing a logical fallacy… [and] by failing to appreciate the crucial difference between "junk DNA" and "garbage DNA."[13]

Some interpreted his attacks as nitpicking over the definition of "function" and quibbling about his arbitrary DNA "junkiness" scale.

"In the social-media age, scientific disagreements can quickly become public—and vitriolic," the science journal *Nature* reported regarding ENCODE's new "framework for quantifying the functional parts of the human genome," which clarified their finding "that 80% of the genome is biochemically functional"…and they narrated Graur's abruptly hostile reaction.[14] He "weighed in on this latest report," saying:

> ENCODE's "stupid claims" from 2012 have finally come to back to [*sic*] "bite them in the proverbial junk"….Through it all, he admittedly showed very little tact. "I believe science is a search for the truth, not a lesson in manners," he says. "I don't do politeness."[14]

By nature, thugs "don't do politeness" by either slashing tires or trashing reputations when enforcing their notion of conformity. Graur-like Darwinists know that research teams often need years to discover the function of one segment of "junk DNA." Since enormous amounts still need careful study, they can use the rest of their lives to coercively defend junk DNA by browbeating others to withdraw conclusions. However, the trend in discovering new functions is decidedly against junk DNA, so they are strong-arming others for a lost cause.

Defend Junk DNA or Risk Supporting Creationists

Zimmer disclosed why Graur and Gregory unleash attacks:

It's no coincidence, researchers like Gregory argue, that bona fide creationists have used recent changes in the thinking about junk DNA to try to turn back the clock to the days before Darwin…whose 1859 book, "On the Origin of Species," set the course for our understanding natural selection as a natural "designer."[15]

Revealing a metaphysical bias, peer-reviewed evolutionary science journals sounded alarms. One published book review savaged the works of two other evolutionists who criticized junk DNA. It warned that "they will also certainly provide ammunition for intelligent design proponents and other creationists. The debunking of junk DNA and the quest to find function for the whole of the human genome have constituted major focus points for such groups in their crusade against evolution."[16]

Graur takes another swipe at ENCODE by reminding Darwinists to respect their theory's highest purpose:

We urge biologists not be afraid of junk DNA. The only people that should be afraid are those claiming that natural processes are insufficient to explain life and that evolutionary theory should be supplemented or supplanted by an intelligent designer….ENCODE's take-home message that everything has a function implies purpose, and purpose is the only thing that evolution cannot provide.[17]

Scientific thuggery aims to intimidate colleagues into silence or bully others into shading their conclusions to not supply "ammunition" against evolution.

Christ's Creative Agency Confirmed

The fact is, evolutionists' definitive declarations that certain enigmatic DNA sequence was junk were spectacularly wrong. Speaking in *Scientific American*, Australian geneticist John Mattick concurred:

> I think this will come to be a classic story of orthodoxy derailing objective analysis of the facts, in this case for a quarter of a century....The failure to recognize the full implications of this [important parallel information derived from non-coding DNA] may well go down as one of the biggest mistakes in the history of molecular biology.[18]

Junk DNA has been exposed as another evolutionary whiff—an embarrassing, science-obstructing swing-and-a-miss.

Notwithstanding reality, Graur-like evolutionists remain hopeful about smashing a home run for Darwin by swinging away in their labs straining to find a junky genome...but that target just gets harder to hit. *Scientific American* forecasts these efforts as vain: "No one knows yet just what the big picture of genetics will look like once this hidden layer of information is made visible. 'Indeed, what was damned as junk because it was not understood may, in fact, turn out to be the very basis of human complexity,' Mattick suggests."[18]

215

Junk DNA amounts to one inning in a bigger contest between two irreconcilable beliefs. One holds that the Lord Jesus Christ exercised creative agency over creatures whose intricate craftsmanship reveals His infinite wisdom and power. The second is a glory-robbing notion that nature exercises agency over organisms through evolutionary tinkering.

Indeed, the known treasures of DNA—and those yet to be discovered—all showcase the Lord Jesus' endless engineering greatness, as implied by ENCODE's continuing search for genetic functions:

> Yet with thousands of cell types to test and a growing set of tools with which to test them, the project could *unfold endlessly.* "We're far from finished," says geneticist Rick Myers of the HudsonAlpha Institute for Biotechnology in Huntsville, Alabama. "You might argue that this could go on *forever.*"[19]

For those with open hearts, the thrill of endless scientific discovery arouses justifiable awe of the Lord's profound mind. "O LORD, how great are Your works! Your thoughts are very deep. A senseless man does not know, nor does a fool understand this" (Psalm 92:5-6).

References
1. Guliuzza, R. 2017. Major Evolutionary Blunders: Evolutionists Strike Out with Imaginary Junk DNA, Part 1. *Acts & Facts.* 46 (4): 16-19.
2. Guliuzza, R. 2015. Major Evolutionary Blunders: The Imaginary Piltdown Man. *Acts & Facts.* 44 (12): 12-14; Guliuzza, R. 2016. Major Evolutionary Blunders: Our Useful Appendix—Evidence of Design, Not Evolution. *Acts & Facts.* 45 (2): 12-14.
3. Collins, F. S. 2006. *The Language of God: A Scientist Presents Evidence for Belief.* New York: Free Press, 137.
4. Zimmer, C. Is Most of Our DNA Garbage? *New York Times.* Posted on nytimes.com March 5, 2015, accessed January 20, 2017.
5. DOE/Lawrence Berkeley National Laboratory. For normal heart function, look beyond the

genes. *ScienceDaily*. Posted on sciencedaily.com October 5, 2016, accessed January 31, 2017.
6. Massachusetts Institute of Technology. Linking RNA structure and function. *ScienceDaily*. Posted on sciencedaily.com September 8, 2016, accessed January 31, 2017.
7. Tomkins, J. P. Junk DNA…Trashed Again. *Creation Science Update*. Posted on ICR.org May 26, 2016, accessed February 13, 2017.
8. Quilez, J. et al. 2016. Polymorphic tandem repeats within gene promoters act as modifiers of gene expression and DNA methylation in humans. *Nucleic Acids Research*. 44 (8): 3750-3762.
9. Tomkins, J. P. Pseudo-Pseudogenes Shake Up Evolutionary Paradigm. *Creation Science Update*. Posted on ICR.org November 14, 2016, accessed February 20, 2017. See also Tomkins, J. P. 2013. Pseudogenes Are Functional, Not Genomic Fossils. *Acts & Facts*. 42 (7): 9.
10. Tomkins, J. P. ENCODE Reveals Incredible Genome Complexity and Function. *Creation Science Update*. Posted on ICR.org September 24, 2012, accessed February 20, 2017; Wells, J. 2011. *The Myth of Junk DNA*. Seattle, WA. Discovery Institute Press
11. Yong, E. ENCODE: the rough guide to the human genome. *Discover Magazine*. Posted on discovermagazine.com September 5, 2012.
12. Zimmer, Is Most of Our DNA Garbage?
13. Graur, D. et al. 2013. On the Immortality of Television Sets: "Function" in the Human Genome According to the Evolution-Free Gospel of ENCODE. *Genome Biology and Evolution*. 5 (3): 578-590.
14. Anonymous. 2014. ENCODE debate revived online. *Nature*. 509 (7499): 137.
15. Zimmer, Is Most of Our DNA Garbage?
16. Marinov, G. K. 2015. A deeper confusion. *Evolution: Education and Outreach*. 8: 22.
17. Graur, On the Immortality of Television Sets.
18. Gibbs, W. W. 2003. The Unseen Genome, Gems among the Junk. *Scientific American*. 289 (5): 26-33.
19. Maher, B. 2012. ENCODE: The human encyclopaedia. *Nature*. 489 (7414): 46-48. Emphasis added.

Image Credits

About the Author

Dr. Randy Guliuzza is a captivating speaker who presents well-documented and often humorous scientific and biblical talks to audiences of all ages. He has represented ICR in several scientific debates at secular universities and in other forums. Dr. Guliuzza has a B.S. in Engineering from the South Dakota School of Mines and Technology, a B.A. in theology from Moody Bible Institute, an M.D. from the University of Minnesota, and a Master of Public Health from Harvard University. Dr. Guliuzza served nine years in the Navy Civil Engineer Corps and is a registered Professional Engineer. In 2008, he retired as Lt. Col. from the U.S. Air Force, where he served as 28th Bomb Wing Flight Surgeon and Chief of Aerospace Medicine. He is the author of *Made in His Image: Examining the Complexities of the Human Body*, *Clearly Seen: Constructing Solid Arguments for Design*, and a contributor to *Guide to Creation Basics*, *Creation Basics & Beyond*, *Guide to the Human Body*, and the *Made in His Image* DVD series.

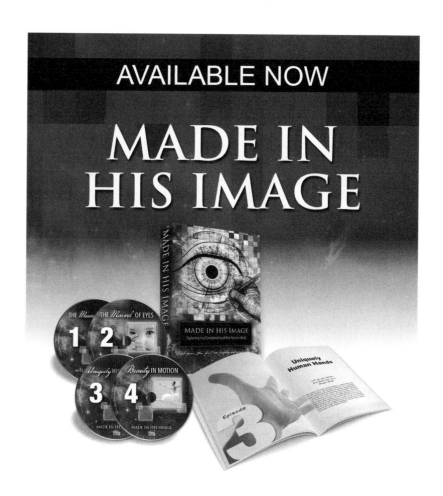